ding

40 W
A Devotional Guide to Pregnancy

Birthing Naturally ✦ 2005

40 Weeks: Devotional Guide to Pregnancy
© 2005 Jennifer Vanderlaan
www.birthingnaturally.net
All Rights Reserved

Published 2005 by Birthing Naturally, Colonie NY 12205
Printed in the United States of America
ISBN10 0-9765541-1-9
ISBN13 978-0-9765541-1-0

This book is available at special quantity discounts for bulk purchases
for educational use, ministry use and fund-raising.   For details, please
email bookdiscounts@birthingnaturally.net.

DISCLAIMER: By reading this book, you agree to educate yourself
about your options and be responsible for the choices you make.   The
author of this book is neither a physician nor a midwife.   This book has
been written to educate and is intended to be used in consultation with
your health care provider.   The publisher and author accept no
responsibility for any loss, damage or injury alleged to be caused by the
information contained in this book.   This book is not a substitute for
professional prenatal care or counseling.

To Jeff
I couldn't have done it without you.

Table of Contents

Acknowledgments

I would like to thank Zola Levitt Ministries, Inc. and Zola Levitt himself through whose work God revealed the correlations between the Jewish feasts and gestation. The devotions discussing these correlations were inspired by two works from Zola Levitt Ministries, Inc., *The Seven Feasts of Israel* and *A Child is Born.* For more information please visit www.levitt.com, or contact them at:

Zola Levitt Ministries, Inc.
PO Box 12268
Dallas TX 75225-0268
1-214-696-8844
1-800-WONDERS

I would like to thank my family, who supported me through endless hours of writing, correcting, editing and planning to get this book to print.

Part One
A Healthy Pregnancy

Do not be wise in your own eyes;
fear the Lord and shun evil.

This will bring health to your body
and nourishment to your bones.

Proverbs 3:7-8

Chapter One
The Process of Pregnancy and Labor

The miracle of a newborn doesn't happen in just a few hours on the birth day. It is a 40 week process of growth and continues past the birth of a child into the first few months postpartum. As your body undergoes physical changes, your spirit grows in faith, trust and capacity to love.

The growth that takes place isn't instant. It happens slowly, along a continuum, with each step preparing you for the next. It is an intricate dance between you and your baby as your bodies communicate and cooperate to move you to the point of birth.

PHYSICAL CHANGES

Your body begins preparing for pregnancy as soon as your menstrual period has begun. A hormone called follicle-stimulating hormone (FSH) prepares a follicle in one of your ovaries to release a mature egg. About 14 days after your menstrual period begins, your body releases Luteinizing

Hormone (Lh) which causes a mature egg to be released into the fallopian tube where it can be fertilized by a sperm.

If the egg is fertilized, the outer covering of the egg, the corpus luteum, grows and begins producing small amounts of progesterone. Progesterone prevents the uterus from contracting to ensure the fertilized egg will not be forced out of the body during a menstrual period. Progesterone also prepares uterine walls to support the pregnancy by increasing the blood vessels in the walls.

About 10 days after fertilization, the egg begins to develop a connection to the uterine wall which will become the placenta. As the placenta grows, it begins producing estrogen. Estrogen causes growth and changes in your uterus, cervix, vagina and breasts. Estrogen also promotes the storage of body fat for extra support during pregnancy. Levels of estrogen increase slowly until about the 12th week when it begins to increase more rapidly.

The hormone human chorionic gonadotropin (hCG) produced by the immature placenta keeps the corpus luteum producing progesterone until about the 12-16th week of pregnancy when hCG levels drop. From the 12th week on, progesterone is made by the placenta, which continues to increase the amounts of progesterone until after your baby is born.

The levels of estrogen and progesterone continue to increase throughout the pregnancy. The increased presence of these hormones causes many changes in your body which help you meet the needs of your baby.

Increased levels of progesterone make your body more sensitive to carbon dioxide in your blood. This is helpful because the carbon dioxide level lets your body know when to take a breath. The increased sensitivity allows you to breathe more frequently, ensuring you have enough oxygen for you and baby. However, as a result of the increased sensitivity, you may feel a shortness of breath from time to time.

Another affect of the increased progesterone is the relaxation of smooth muscle systems in your body. This is helpful because your circulatory system is smooth muscle, and the decreased tone of your blood vessels allows them to carry more blood, accommodating your increased blood volume. However, your digestive tract is also smooth muscle and it becomes relaxed as well, so you may feel more frequent indigestion, heartburn or constipation.

The increased levels of estrogen help your body to support the growth of the uterus by increasing the number of cells in the uterus, the size of the cells and the blood flow to the uterus. The uterine veins enlarge to 60 times their normal size which allows for adequate drainage of your baby's waste products from the uterine environment.

Estrogen also helps support your baby by increasing the blood volume and increasing the available proteins in your blood so your baby gets all he needs to grow. However, the increased estrogen levels cause a decrease in available gastric acid and pepsin for digestion, so you may have more frequent digestive upsets.

As your pregnancy progresses, the placenta produces larger amounts of a hormone called relaxin. Relaxin loosens the joints of your pelvis to ensure it has an adequate stretch to allow your baby an exit. However, relaxin doesn't just affect the joints of the pelvis, so you may find that you begin to feel wobbly all over as your knees, hips, shoulders and wrists feel loose.

As your baby nears readiness for birth, his brain and placenta begin releasing a series of hormones that cause his body to produce oxytocin which stimulates the uterus. These same hormones cause his adrenal glands to mature so they can produce cortisol, a hormone that stimulates the lungs to finish maturing.

While this is happening, these same hormones increase your estrogen production.   As estrogen production increases, it increases the uterine sensitivity to oxytocin, which is being pumped into your blood stream by the baby. You will slowly begin to feel Braxton-Hicks contractions in response to the oxytocin.   These contractions help to strengthen the uterine muscle for labor.

Another effect of the increase in estrogen is the increase of prostaglandins. Prostaglandins help to soften or "ripen" the cervix (opening of the uterus) so it will be ready to stretch to allow the baby to pass through.   With the increase of uterine activity and the ripening of the cervix, you may find you have completed some of the necessary work of opening the cervix before you actually begin labor.

As your cervix, uterus and vagina are stimulated and stretched by the contractions and increased prostaglandin levels, your pituitary gland is stimulated to release oxytocin. How your body begins labor is a mystery only God understands, but it seems the increase in prostaglandins and oxytocin start contractions which then increase the levels of prostaglandins and oxytocin further for even more contractions.   This cycle continues to build on itself until your baby is born.

In this intricate dance of gestation, you and your baby work together to allow your body to provide everything he needs to grow. You continue to work in a partnership to prepare your body to give birth and his body to be born until at last, you work as a team to get him in your arms. All through this miracle of life, the Holy Spirit will be working on your heart.

SPIRITUAL CHANGES

It is not coincidence pregnancy lasts 40 weeks. In the Bible, the number 40 signifies a time of testing or trial. It rained for 40 days and 40 nights, Moses was on the mountain for 40 days, the Israelites wandered in the desert for 40 years, Jesus was tempted in the desert for 40 days and he was seen for 40 days after his death before ascending to Heaven. God will use these 40 weeks of pregnancy to test and grow your faith.

You will find yourself questioning what is most important to you, who you want to be and what legacy you want to pass on to the next generation. You will be faced with real life decisions in which you are able to sacrifice your desires for the good of your child. You will find the day to day struggles give you opportunities to grow in your faith like never before. On top of all this is the fact that God has entrusted one of his children to your care.

We are encouraged to mature ourselves as Christians by strengthening certain character traits. 2 Peter 1:5-8 tells us:

For this very reason, make every effort to add to your faith goodness; and to goodness, knowledge; and to knowledge, self-control; and to self-control, perseverance; and to perseverance, godliness; and to godliness, brotherly kindness; and to brotherly kindness, love. For if you possess these qualities in increasing measure, they will keep you from being ineffective and unproductive in your knowledge of our Lord Jesus Christ.

This time of pregnancy gives you unique opportunities to grow these characteristics in yourself. Pregnancy also gives you a natural desire to improve your character. That is one of the most amazing things about pregnancy – you want to grow and you are more able to grow than most any other time in life!

Faith

If faith is being sure of what you hope for and certain of what you cannot see (Hebrews 11:1), then the naturally mysterious qualities of pregnancy give you exactly what you need to build your faith. You cannot see the baby, but you are certain he is there. You have no real way of proving the baby is healthy, but you trust your instincts.

As your pregnancy progresses and the discomforts that come along begin to take more attention your faith and trust in God grows. You have faith the pregnancy is for a purpose and the discomforts will go away. Your body changes shape, you suddenly realize your life is going to change forever and once again your faith is forced to grow as you face the unexpected future.

Your faith will continue to build, and labor will be an amazing time of faith building. As you work with your body and trust that God is in control, you may find the contractions leave you fearful. Your faith in God, having been built up over the previous nine months will be your strength as you trust in God's plan and allow him to use labor to draw you closer to him.

Goodness

One of the first things all children learn is that parents who teach by words instead of by example don't really believe what they teach. Do as I say, not as I do parenting is ineffective at best, and can damage your child's faith in you as a trustworthy person. Now that you are pregnant, you may be thinking about who you want your children to be, how you want them to act and how you want them to serve God.

Goodness can be considered moral excellence, and if this is something you want to pass on to your children, you must possess it first. If you have any rough edges or character traits you don't want to see in your children, now is the time to begin changing them. God can use this natural desire to pass goodness onto your children to help you break some habits you have been struggling with. Welcome the Holy Spirit into your life and ask him to let you see clearly any areas you need to change, and to give you the strength and courage to make these changes.

Knowledge

In this reference, the knowledge referred to is scriptural knowledge, knowledge of the Word of God. Although most expectant parents are thirsty for knowledge about the changes they will soon be experiencing, God can use this quest for accurate information to help you increase your study of the Bible.

You may begin to notice some differences in families at your church or in your extended family, and it may cause you to wonder how a family should best operate. Or you may begin to wonder what God expects of you as a mother.

These are great topics of study and can be examined in depth in the Bible.

As you near your baby's birth day, it may suddenly seem as if it isn't enough to just copy what other families are doing. You are responsible to God for the choices you make and the way you raise his child. Let this desire for knowledge bring you deeper into God's Word, searching for what he desires of you.

Self-Control

Pregnancy is a time where you have no choice but to develop stronger self-control. Some women give up unhealthy habits, or activities that may harm their child such as smoking or drinking alcohol. With the increased fatigue, you have no choice but to be disciplined in your resting. Many women find they need to change the way they eat to keep their bodies operating well.

Many women also find pregnancy causes them to feel more irritable and get frustrated easier. Again, this is a natural opportunity to practice self-control. Instead of treating others harshly because of a bad mood or irritableness, you should strive to continue to treat others in love.

Perseverance

With all the normal discomforts and changes in pregnancy, plus the fact that to give birth you need to wait nine months, this is a perfect time to develop perseverance. Some women find they not only bear with their pregnancy, but actually enjoy this special time. It isn't that these women don't experience the pregnancy symptoms other women have. They simply choose to allow the symptoms to remind them of the blessing they are carrying. They are willing to persevere because the goal is always kept in the front of their minds.

As you get closer to your baby's birth day, you may find your need for patience and perseverance increases greatly. There is a correlation between the decreasing time until your baby's birth and the increasing desire to have your baby be born. Whether you like it or not you will develop perseverance because you cannot rush your baby.

Godliness

Being a part of the creation of another eternal soul will build your respect and admiration for God. As you witness the growth of your baby, see your abdomen fill and feel the movements of little arms and legs inside you, the sense of wonder and amazement at the power of God grows.

There is a danger during pregnancy to struggle with "having a form of godliness but denying its power" (2 Timothy 3:5). It is so easy to watch what is happening inside you and attribute the power to some nameless force of nature, or the power of your body. When this happens a woman develops respect and admiration for the process of pregnancy and birth instead of the God who designed it.

Brotherly Kindness

Pregnancy is also a time when you are challenged to build friendship bonds with other women. God has designed pregnancy and childbirth in such a way that it is to our benefit to spend time with other women and build relationships with others. Not only relationships where you depend on the help of others, but also cherished friendships where you share with each other, encourage each other and challenge each other.

You will be able to build bonds with your baby through prenatal play and interactions. This prenatal parenting helps to grow your ability to cherish another person, to look forward to the friendly interactions with another person. The word that means brotherly kindness is one of the Greek words for love.

Love

The word used for love, agape, means the sacrificial and unconditional love God loves us with. In essence it is meeting the needs of others before your own. It includes treating others with mercy, grace and forgiveness, and offering of yourself without expecting anything in return.

What an amazing opportunity pregnancy gives us to practice agape love. You will be making decisions not based on how it will benefit you, but how it will impact your child, and this is before you even get a glimpse of his face. Your baby is powerless to offer anything in return for the sacrifices you make, and yet you will be filled with joy and happiness sometimes simply by feeling the very kicks you endure in love.

As you move further through pregnancy the common discomforts become more frequent and longer lasting. The growing impact they have on your life increases your opportunity to grow in love through your attitude and decisions. It builds right through labor, when you will again be faced with decisions that will influence both you and your baby. Pregnancy and childbirth are natural times to mature into a more agape loving person.

I can not imagine that Moses would be too distracted in a field with sheep that he wouldn't notice a burning bush (Exodus 3:4). In fact, I would think the quietness and opportunity to be enjoying nature would make shepherding the perfect time for God to start talking and Moses to start listening.

But God did not just start talking. He waited for the burning bush to get Moses' attention so he would approach God.

Pregnancy is like a burning bush in that it causes us to stop and pay attention. It is a time when most women look inside their heart and their lives and question who they are and who they want to be. As you ask yourself, "What do I want to pass on to my child," or, "Is this the kind of life I want my child to live?" understand these questions are not simply from yourself. God is using this fertile time to grow not only a baby, but also your soul.

When God got Moses' attention he sent him off to Egypt to free the Hebrew slaves. The Bible tells us Moses fought the command of God, asking him to send someone else instead. Although he worshiped God, Moses didn't necessarily want his life to change. I remind you of this so you will not be surprised if God asks you to change your life. I also don't want you to be surprised if you initially fight the changes God may ask you to make.

Chapter Two
Stewardship

For most expectant parents, the strongest desire is for a healthy baby. Although there are some aspects of your child's health you will have no control over, your daily lifestyle habits have a tremendous impact on your baby's overall health and development.

God sets forth a principle of stewardship in Matthew 25: 14-30, the *Parable of the Talents*. In this story, Jesus demonstrates that as caretakers of the things God has given us, we have a responsibility to make the best choices possible. This is not solely a financial responsibility, but can be considered a principle by which to live your life.

You have been given many gifts by God. Among those gifts right now are your money, time, food, baby, and health. God calls us to make the best use of the resources he provides for us. Whether you have been given a little or a lot, God does set a standard that you are to use the things he has given you wisely. When relating this parable to your pregnancy, being a good steward means making the best health choices available to you.

Understand that what is considered the best option is not always available to you. Sometimes issues such as location, finances or health limit the choices you have when faced with a decision. God is not calling you to reach for what you cannot have. Instead he is asking you to make the best use of what is available. You don't have to keep up with the Jones', and you don't have to make all the same decisions that your sister or neighbor or friend made during her pregnancy. But you do need to consider all your options, understanding how each possibility can impact you and your baby.

NUTRITION

What you eat can have more of an impact on your overall health than any other health habit. However, ensuring you eat a healthy variety of foods can take more time than any other health habit. Nutrition is also an area where family and friends are likely to give unsolicited advice, and not all of it is good. How do you make the time to eat well? And for that matter, just what do you need to eat to "eat well?"

Understanding good nutrition begins with understanding why your body needs food. Food is not just the energy your body uses to keep itself going, food also supplies the building blocks of the system. You've probably heard the analogy that your body needs food like your car needs gas. Actually, food is more important to your body than the gas is to a car. Food is more like filling the gas tank, putting on new tires, checking the alignment, changing the oil, installing fresh spark plugs, topping off the fluids, rebuilding the motor and finishing with a wash and wax.

The food you eat is broken down into useable parts by your digestive system and then is transferred by your blood to the areas of your body that need materials that can only be supplied by food. Some of these materials are used to build muscles, some build blood, others are used to make hormones, and some are needed to keep the system running properly.

Your body works on an amazing balance. Many of the materials your body needs must be consumed every day to remain healthy. However, extra or unneeded materials are simply not absorbed into the blood stream, or are removed from the blood stream. Because of this, you cannot give your body junk foods for several meals in a row and then gorge yourself on healthy food to try to make up for it. In addition to feeling awful, your body will suffer by storing the extra calories (unused energy in the food you eat) as fat in case you don't have enough to eat later.

Being pregnant adds another issue to the balance of eating well because many women find they are unable to eat their regular meals due to nausea or indigestion. To get the volume of food needed to support the health of mother and baby, pregnant women will eat smaller meals more often throughout the day. However, when you are eating what feels like snacks instead of meals, it can be easy to fool yourself into thinking you are eating healthy when you are consuming mostly junk foods.

The best way to ensure adequate nutrition is to pay attention to what you eat. Reading the information is not enough. By setting aside time to plan some menus and a shopping list you increase your chances of eating healthy. If you take a little more time and prepare some fruits and vegetables to keep in the refrigerator for snacks you will again increase your chances of eating healthy. If you buy raw, whole foods and take the time to prepare meals from fresh ingredients you once again increase your chances of eating healthy.

You may not have the time, energy or money to put into completely changing your eating. That's ok. Remember, God only holds you accountable for what he has given you. Ask God to show you changes you can make to improve your overall health and he will be faithful to answer. Even small changes in the way you eat can have a big impact on your baby.

EXERCISE

The body is made for movement. The more our muscles are worked, the stronger they become. The more we stretch, the more flexible our bodies become. But exercise during pregnancy doesn't just keep you strong; it can actually keep you more comfortable.

Women who exercise feel more energy throughout the day. Exercises such as walking actually help stimulate the digestive system to help prevent digestive discomforts during pregnancy. Staying active can help you sleep better at night so you are well rested for the next day. Studies have even found women who exercised during pregnancy had shorter labors.

Once again you must consider what options God has provided for you. It may not be possible for you to join a gym or purchase exercise equipment for your use at home, however there are other options for exercise God has made available to you. As the steward of your physical health it is your job to make the best possible choices regarding exercise.

Some options may be walking on a lunch break at work or riding a stationary bike while you talk on the phone. You may find an exercise video in your own home is a good option for you, or you may choose to hire a personal trainer at a local gym. Perhaps there is a local pool you can use for swimming or you can participate in a group sport.

The American College of Obstetricians and Gynecologists has issued recommendations for exercise during pregnancy that place few limits on the activities a healthy pregnant woman should participate in. Take a look at your options and be a wise steward who invests well in your health.

PRENATAL CARE

Another area where you must weigh your options and discern the best choice is your prenatal care. Depending on your location, you may have few choices or you may have many. Regardless of what options are available to you, God is calling you to make the best possible decision about using the services he provides.

One decision will be the caregiver you choose. Your community may have midwives that assist in home births, midwives and obstetricians who assist in hospital births, midwives or physicians who work through a birth center, family practice physicians who will assist during labors or any other combination. Be sure to interview several different care providers before making your choice.

It is important to remember the caregiver you hire will affect almost every other decision you make about this pregnancy. Her advice and recommendations will help you choose how to handle common and perhaps not so common situations. Take the time to learn about her philosophy of pregnancy and birth, how she assists during labor, what she considers problems and how she handles them.

Another issue that sometimes arises is choosing one caregiver from a group practice when you don't care for the rest of the members. Weigh this decision carefully to be sure this is the best option God has given you. Are the other members of the practice simply not as good a fit with you, or do they really rub you the wrong way? Is there another practice that has more caregivers you feel comfortable with? Can you be a client of only one member of the practice?

Some women feel their options are limited to the caregivers listed with their insurance service. These care providers are not your only options; they are simply the options your insurance service will pay for. You do have the freedom to go outside your insurance service if you feel you will get better care that way. Again, weigh this decision carefully to be sure you have found the best option God has given you.

You will also need to make decisions about what tests you would like to have performed during pregnancy. As the client, you always have the right to refuse any service you are not interested in. After taking the time to explore the options available to you, be sure you consider why you might like each test. Will the information you gather be useful to you? Will the results cause you to make a change in anything you are currently doing? Is there more than one way to perform the test?

At some point in your pregnancy it may become apparent that what seemed like the best choice wasn't. If so, simply make the necessary changes to continue to be a good steward of the services God is providing for you.

HARMFUL SUBSTANCES

Some of the provisions God has made for you during pregnancy are not things you should run to, but instead things you should stay away from. Some substances can harm you or your baby, and God has given you the ability to stay away from most of them.

Alcohol and cigarette smoke and illegal drugs can cause problems for an unborn baby, as can over the counter and prescription medications. It is best to avoid these when possible. If the need for a medication arises, work with your caregiver to determine the least harmful option. You may find what you thought could only be cured with medication may be handled comfortably with a change in diet, exercise or some other lifestyle change.

Some women develop sensitivities to chemicals while pregnant, and so many household tasks must be ignored or done with less harmful substances such as vinegar and baking soda. Other women find their diet consists mostly of pre-packaged food which contains chemicals that are untested regarding safety in pregnancy. There are also women who work in jobs that expose them to chemicals that may be harmful to the unborn. If you have any concerns about a substance, simply avoid it. It may be the Holy Spirit prompting you to keep your baby out of harm's way.

POTENTIAL PROBLEMS

Being a good steward of the health and pregnancy God has given you isn't just about selecting the best options. It is also about being the caretaker and watchman for your health. You should be aware of the most common signs of problems in pregnancy and how to get help if necessary.

Part of stewardship is knowing when you can handle the situation and when to ask for help. Seeking medical guidance when you are concerned for your health is not a lack of faith, it is simply an act of stewardship. Investing time in discovering what the problem is and what options may be available allows you to make the best decision about how to handle a problem.

Chapter Three
Pregnancy Nutrition

The very food you eat becomes the building blocks for your baby. Eating a highly nutritious diet gives your baby the best start possible. The next three chapters will provide you with the tools you need to assess your diet and make any changes you feel are necessary.

GOOD NUTRITION

The principles of good nutrition do not change because you are pregnant. At the most basic level, the food you eat is absorbed into your bloodstream by your digestive system and used as needed. How a particular food is used varies depending on the food's composition.

All foods are made up of a combination of carbohydrates, proteins, fats and water. Some foods are high in carbohydrates, some are high in proteins and some are high in fat. In addition to the main components of the food, each food contains a variety of vitamins and minerals, and may contain fiber. Each component plays a different role in your body.

Carbohydrates

Carbohydrates (carbs) are the body's main source of energy and should be a major part of total daily intake. There are two types of carbohydrates: simple carbohydrates (such as sugar or honey) and complex carbohydrates (such as grains, beans, peas, or potatoes).

Both simple and complex carbohydrates are broken down by the body into blood sugar (glucose); however, nutritionally speaking, complex carbohydrates are better for you. This is because simple sugars are digested quickly, and most foods with simple sugars contain very few vitamins and minerals. Complex carbohydrates on the other hand take longer to digest and are good sources of fiber, vitamins and minerals. Complex carbohydrate foods are generally a better nutritional value for the number of calories they contain, and tend to be more satisfying than simple carbohydrates.

Proteins

Protein supplies amino acids to build and maintain healthy body tissue. There are 20 amino acids considered essential because the body must have all of them in the right amounts to function properly. Twelve of these are manufactured in the body but the other eight amino acids must be provided by the diet. Foods from animal sources such as milk or eggs often contain all these essential amino acids while a variety of plant products must be taken together to provide all these necessary protein components.

Unlike carbohydrates which can be stored as fat, your body has no mechanism to store extra protein. The unused proteins are broken down until they can be made into fat, and the part that makes it a protein is then excreted from the body. If you do not eat enough protein to repair your body and build your baby, your body will begin to break down its own tissues to get building blocks for your baby and neither you nor your baby will have what you need to keep your bodies healthy. Contrary to popular belief, your baby cannot be built from extra stores of fat on your body.

Every day you need about .4 grams of protein for each pound of body weight (0.8 g of protein per kilogram of body weight). So a 140 pound woman should eat about 56 grams of protein a day when she is not pregnant. When you are pregnant your protein need increases. Dr. Thomas Brewer, an expert on pregnancy nutrition, recommends that you aim for 80–100 grams of protein every day while pregnant.

Fats

Fat supplies energy and transports nutrients. There are two families of fatty acids considered essential for the body: the omega-3 and omega-6 fatty acids. Essential fatty acids are required by the body to function normally. They can be obtained from canola oil, flaxseed oil, cold-water fish, or fish oil, all of which contain omega-3 fatty acids, and primrose or black currant seed oil, which contains omega-6 fatty acids.

Vitamins and Minerals

Vitamins are organic substances present in food and required by the body in a minute amount for regulation of metabolism and maintenance of normal growth and functioning. The most commonly known vitamins are A, B1 (thiamine), B2 (riboflavin), B3 (niacin), B5 (pantothenic acid), B6 (pyridoxine), B7 (biotin), B9 (folic acid), B12 (cobalamin), C (ascorbic acid), D, E, and K. The B and C vitamins are water-soluble, excess amounts of which are excreted in the urine. The A, D, E, and K vitamins are fat-soluble and will be stored in the body fat.

Minerals are vital to our existence because they are used to make up muscles, tissues, and bones. They also are important components of many life-supporting systems, such as hormones, oxygen transport, and enzyme systems.

Fiber

Fiber is the material that gives plants texture and support. Although it is primarily made up of carbohydrates, it does not have a lot of calories and usually is not broken down by the body for energy. Dietary fiber is found in plant foods such as fruits, vegetables, legumes, nuts, and whole grains.

There are two types of fiber: soluble and insoluble. Insoluble fiber, as the name implies, does not dissolve in water because it contains a high amount of cellulose. Insoluble fiber can be found in the bran of grains, the pulp of fruit and the skin of vegetables. Soluble fiber is the type of fiber that dissolves in water. It can be found in a variety of fruits and vegetables such as apples, oatmeal and oat bran, rye flour, and dried beans.

Although they share some common characteristics such as being partially digested in the stomach and intestines and have few calories, each type of fiber has its own specific health benefits. Insoluble fiber speeds up the transit of foods through the digestive system and adds bulk to the stools which helps treat constipation or diarrhea and prevents colon cancer. Only soluble fiber attaches itself to blood cholesterol so it can be eliminated from the body.

Water

Water helps to regulate body temperature, transports nutrients to cells, and rids the body of waste materials.

SELECTING FOODS

The key to good nutrition is getting the right mix of protein, carbohydrates, fats, vitamins, minerals and fiber. This means you will need to eat a variety of foods so you can "balance" the nutrients in your diet. Along with the nutrient composition, every food has a calorie value. The calorie is the basic measure of energy in the food. A food with 400 calories stores more energy than a food with 200 calories.

The energy in the food is used by your body to complete its daily activities such as digestion, growth, physical movement, thinking, breathing, circulation and repair of tissues. Calories you consume that are not used by your body are stored as body fat, because it is the easiest way to store and retrieve large amounts of calories for later use. When you do not consume enough calories in a day, your body breaks down some of the stored fat to use as energy.

Because having excess body fat decreases your overall health and increases your risk for many diseases, you will want to avoid eating excess calories. However, you will still need to fulfill your body's daily requirements for the basic nutrients. Understand that the amount of calories you eat says very little about the quality of nutrition you receive. You can be overfed (eating too many calories) and be undernourished (not meeting your daily requirements for basic nutrients).   To meet your nutritional needs without overeating you will want to choose foods that are a high nutritional value for the calories.

A high value food is one that provides a variety of nutrients in a reasonable amount of calories. These foods are generally lower in fat and sugars which provide extra calories without providing higher amounts of nutrients. For example, when planning a breakfast you could choose to eat 2 scrambled eggs, one cup of oatmeal, 1 cup of fat free milk and a medium orange which would cost you about 451 calories, or you could eat 2 Pop Tarts and a cup of coffee with 1 packet of sugar which would cost you about 435 calories. Nutritionally, each meal will give you:

Nutrient	Eggs	Pop Tarts
Protein	29 g	5 g
Carbohydrates	56 g	81 g
Fiber	7 g	2 g
Fat	13 g	11 g
Vitamin A	376.8 re	298.5 RE
Vitamin C	72.4 mg	.3 mg
Folate	95.4 mcg	83.4 mcg
Calcium	470.8 mg	30.6 mg
Iron	3.1	3.7 mg
Magnesium	113.5 mg	27.6 mg
Potassium	940 mg	212 mg
Sodium	831 mg	439 mg

It is easy to see that some foods are better nutritional values for the calories. Because pregnancy can be a time when it is difficult to eat normal amounts of food at meals, it becomes even more important that the foods you eat are nutritionally packed.

The foods with the highest nutritional value will be foods that are as close to their natural state as possible. Calorie for calorie, fresh fruits are more nutritionally packed than fruit juices or fruits packed in syrup. Vegetables that are steamed, grilled or eaten raw provide more nutrients per calorie than vegetables that are fried or served with cream or sauces. Processed vegetables, such as boxes of "instant" side dishes or meals often contain extra fats and sugars that increase the calorie content without increasing the nutritive value.

Low fat dairy products provide the same nutrients as full fat versions for less calories. Lactose free products provide the same nutrients for people who have trouble digesting lactose. There is a wide variation in the nutritive value of yogurts available today, so read labels carefully. Lean fresh meats provide more nutrition for fewer calories than processed meats such as hot dogs and luncheon meats.

Whole grains are more nutritionally dense and balanced than refined grains. Eating a side of brown rice or quinoa provides more nutrients for the calories than having a roll or slice of bread. Many foods, such as baked goods, prepared from refined grains provide very little nutrition while they supply high amounts of calories.

Learn to read labels while you shop and compare foods. As you try to include nutritionally packed foods in your diet, you will really need to take an honest look at the way your family has been eating. If most of your food comes in boxes that can be prepared in three easy steps, then your first change may simply be to start having meals made from raw ingredients two or three nights a week. If you are already cooking from raw ingredients, you may need to take a look at the quality of the ingredients, and make a switch to more nutritionally packed varieties like lean meats or fish instead of ground beef and whole grains instead of refined grains.

ALTERNATIVES

> *Romans 14:1-4 Accept him whose faith is weak, without passing judgment on disputable matters. One man's faith allows him to eat everything, but another man, whose faith is weak, eats only vegetables. The man who eats everything must not look down on him who does not, and the man who does not eat everything must not condemn the man who does, for God has accepted him. Who are you to judge someone else's servant? To his own master he stands or falls. And he will stand, for the Lord is able to make him stand.*

For many Christians the foods they choose to eat or choose to abstain from are not determined purely by their assumed nutritional content. If you believe God has called you to abstain from certain foods then you should continue to abstain from those foods. If you believe God has allowed you to eat all foods, feel free to eat any food.

You select the foods you want to eat from the choices God has given you based on the guidelines of a balanced diet. Your location, your income or your taste buds may limit you from choosing some foods and that is not a problem. God does not expect you to use what he has not made available to you. When choosing foods, be sure to select foods of high nutritional quality and remember to eat 80-100 grams of protein per day.

Chapter Five
Planning Meals

The secret to successfully eating a healthy diet is proper planning. Ensuring you get adequate amounts of protein, vitamins and minerals will require you have healthy choices available, balance your meals through out the day, and are aware of the foods you are eating. With a little effort, you can improve your diet and still eat most of the foods you love.

BALANCED DIET

The actual amount of food that you need each day will be dependant on your size and activity level. The suggestions given here are simply guidelines for you to use as you work to determine how much food your body needs each day to be healthy.

Remember the serving size recommended is not the same as what you may consider a helping of a food. One slice of bread is one serving of a grain product, so you will get two servings when you eat a sandwich. If you use large slices of bread or rolls, you may be eating 4 or 6 servings of grains in one sandwich.

Since your baby needs good quality protein every day, it is a good idea to begin your meal planning by making a list of your favorite and most easily accessible protein foods. Think of the eggs, dairy, meat and vegetable proteins you consume on a regular basis. Make a list of how you would eat them at breakfast, lunch, dinner and for snacks. Once you have your list, put together one or two days of meals aiming for about the following averages:

Suggested Servings

Grains	5-6 (1 ounce servings)
Fruits	2 (1 cup servings)
Vegetables	3 (3/4 cup servings)
Dairy	3 (1 cup servings)
Meat, fish, beans and eggs	2-3 (2-3 ounce servings)

Remember, the guidelines are the average amounts of food you should eat each day, if you normally eat more then plan for more food. The guidelines can be broken up to fit your eating schedule. If you prefer to eat 5 or 6 small meals a day, then use the guidelines to plan 5 or 6 meals.

Do not try to consume less in an effort to control your weight gain. The amount of weight you gain is not an indicator of the nutritive value of your diet. You can gain weight eating nothing but potato chips and cola, but your body will not be healthy. Concentrate instead on choosing good foods and eating enough to satisfy your body's needs.

Focus not only on getting the right number of servings from each food group, but also on eating a variety of foods from each group. For example, when selecting fruits and vegetables try to eat a few different colors each day. This helps to ensure you get all the vitamins and minerals.

WHAT IS A SERVING

Serving size varies for each type of food. The most accurate measure is to check the label when available, and to use a small food scale. The following list should help you ensure you are eating a serving instead of a helping.

A serving from the grain group is 1 to 1 ½ ounce, which is 1 slice of bread, ½ an English muffin or hamburger roll, about 1 cup of ready to eat cereal or ½ cup of cooked cereal, pasta or rice.

A serving of a vegetable is 1 cup of raw leafy vegetables or ½ cup of other vegetables whether cooked or raw. You may also count ¾ cup of vegetable juice as one serving.

A serving of fruit is 1 medium fruit (about the size of your fist) or ½ cup of chopped, cooked or canned fruit. You may also count ¾ cup of fruit juice as one serving.

A serving of dairy food is 1 cup of milk or yogurt. You may also count 1 ½ ounces of a natural cheese or 2 ounces of a processed cheese as one serving.

A serving of meat is 2-3 ounces, roughly the size of a deck of cards. You may also count ½ cup of cooked beans or tofu, 1 egg, 2 tablespoons of peanut butter or 1/3 cup of nuts.

Here is a sample menu with foods I like to eat that follows the good eating guidelines. For more sample menus and meal ideas check out the nutrition section at www.birthingnaturally.net:

SAMPLE MENU

Breakfast:
    ½ C Cooked Oatmeal
    8 oz. Milk
    ½ C Sliced Strawberries

Snack:
    2 oz. Cheddar Cheese Melted on a Tortilla

Lunch:
    Spinach Salad (With 2 Hard Boiled Eggs)
    Chicken & Vegetable Soup with Barley
    8 oz. Milk

Snack:
    1 Orange and a Bran Muffin

Dinner:
    3 oz. Grilled Salmon
    1 C Steamed Broccoli
    ½ C Brown Rice

Snack:
    8 oz. Yogurt with Fruit

SNACKING

Because pregnancy decreases the available room for your stomach to expand and hold food, snacking becomes a must to ensure you get enough food during the day. Think of your snacks as mini-meals and use them to help you meet your daily nutrient requirements.

For example, if you find protein foods are the hardest for you to work into your menus, try snacking on mixed nuts, deviled eggs, bean soup, bean dip, slices of turkey or chicken breast, a protein shake or a protein bar. If you find all you eat from the grain group is dry cereal and pasta, you may benefit from trying bran muffins, toasted whole wheat English muffins, air-popped popcorn, whole-grain crackers, or granola bars.

Make sure you get the calcium and other nutrients you need by snacking on cheese sticks, cheese and crackers, yogurt with dried fruit or nuts, cottage cheese with fruit or instant pudding. And as an added bonus, most dairy foods are a good source of protein as well.

Each type of produce has its own secret formula of nutrients that cannot be copied with supplements, so it is important that you eat a variety of fruits and vegetables every day. Snacking from the fruit and vegetable group gives you the opportunity to combine a variety of foods. Mix frozen fruit with juice in your blender for a fruit smoothie. Keep a tray of cut up vegetables in the refrigerator. Keep a pot of vegetable soup in the refrigerator. Many fruits are easily portable and delicious eaten raw.

QUICK MEAL IDEAS

Even with the best planning, some days you simply don't have the time or energy to prepare a big meal. However, you can't skip eating healthy. Here are some very easy to prepare foods that can help prevent you from running to the fast food drive through when you are hungry:

- Bowl of Cereal, toast with peanut butter, milk
- Cottage cheese with fruit
- Yogurt with fruit and granola
- Grilled cheese sandwich, salad or fresh vegetables
- Slice of cheese, English muffin or toast, piece of fruit
- Tuna sandwich, fruit
- Mixed nuts, piece of cheese, glass of juice
- Dry cereal with yogurt
- Peanut butter and jelly sandwich, fresh vegetables
- Instant soup or can of soup
- Popcorn, piece of cheese, piece of fruit

MAKING HEALTHY COOKING EASIER

There are a lot of reasons why pregnancy is a difficult time to eat healthy. The lack of energy, slowed digestion and food aversions some women get can wreak havoc on a healthy diet. There are a few tricks you might find helpful as you begin to make changes to your diet.

Keep your refrigerator and pantry well stocked. You don't need to keep a month of groceries in the house, but making sure you have a few key items on hand at all times can really improve your eating. Shop once a week to make it easier to keep on hand fresh fruits and vegetables that spoil quickly. As you shop, keep in mind how many servings of each piece of produce you will need for one week. Pay attention each week to which foods are left over and which foods you ran out of so you can gauge how much of a food you actually eat in a week.

Choose your least busy day to shop so you have time to prepare your fruits and vegetables when you return home. Take the time to wash your fresh fruit and put it in a bowl for easy snacking. Also cut up your vegetables for snacks or salad and keep them in the refrigerator so they will be ready when you are hungry. Make up a pot of soup to keep in the refrigerator for a quick meal. You are more likely to eat a food that is already prepared and ready to be eaten.

Use your freezer to store leftovers you make intentionally. It takes very little extra time to double a recipe, but it will give you an extra meal. Invest in good quality containers that will allow you to freeze a meal for use later in the week or month when you don't have the time or desire to cook.

Grilling is a healthy way to prepare meats, it cooks relatively quickly and the smells stay outdoors. A gas grill makes the process very fast, working as easily as your stove and can be purchased through most home stores for about $100. In addition to meats, you can also grill vegetables so in the summer you don't have to heat the house to eat.

If you find you snack on chips and cookies, start experimenting with more nutritious and satisfying snacks. Cheese and crackers are easy to keep on hand and can satisfy a craving. Peanuts are easily transported and so are many fresh fruits. Keep vegetables and bean dips in your refrigerator. Instead of cookies and muffins, think yogurt and dried fruit. Instead of ice cream, try a fruit and yogurt smoothie. You will find they give you the sweetness you want, but also provide you with protein and nutrients to keep you and your baby healthy.

Eat when you are hungry, even if it is not a meal time. You will gain weight during pregnancy, and it is healthy to do so. It is not healthy to starve yourself and your growing baby of the food you both need desperately. However some women use eating as a way to manage stress or fulfill other emotional needs. Not only will overeating increase your risk of health problems, it will also increase the discomfort you feel from indigestion and heartburn. Before you grab a snack, ask yourself "Am I really hungry?" If the answer is no, then find some other way to fill the emotional need.

If you are really having difficulty preparing food, ask your family and friends to each prepare a dish for you to freeze. Most won't mind doing it, and you should have enough food to last you a couple weeks. By that time, your energy level and ability to stomach raw ingredients may have improved.

Chapter Six
Pregnancy Exercise

Staying healthy during pregnancy increases your chances of remaining low-risk. Being low-risk allows you the most options possible for labor and giving birth. Along with eating a well balanced diet, exercise is a key ingredient to a healthy pregnancy.

The benefits of exercise during pregnancy are amazing. A 1992 study by Lois Jovanovic-Peterson found mothers who were experiencing gestational diabetes could lower their blood sugar levels to the point that they no longer needed insulin shots by doing aerobic exercise for 20-30 minutes three times a week.

Dr. Tanya K. Sorensen reported in a poster session at the 2002 annual meeting of the Society for Maternal-Fetal Medicine that vigorous exercise during pregnancy appears to reduce the risk of preeclampsia.

As for labor, a study reported in the Family Practice Research Journal in 1991 showed that mothers who exercised 20 minutes three times a week for at least 20 weeks of their pregnancy had shorter second stages and fewer complications during labor than mothers who didn't exercise.

James Clapp, M.D. reported in 1996 that women who exercised during pregnancy had their babies an average of 5 days earlier than non-exercisers and had less need for medical intervention. In his paper to The American Journal of Sports Medicine he stated, "The active phase of their labors is about 2 hours shorter, clinical and laboratory evidence of fetal stress is decreased, and the incidence of operative delivery (forceps or cesarean section) is reduced from 48% to 14%."

Staying fit and healthy can also improve the outcomes for your baby. In 1993 Maureen C. Hatch and her coworkers at Columbia University in New York City found mothers who exercised tended to have bigger babies, which can mean the babies are better fit to handle illnesses.

In a 1997 study out of Case Western Reserve University James Clopp, M.D. found that by age 5, the babies of mothers who exercised for at least 30 minutes three times a week had lower levels of body fat and scored higher on the Wechsler test of general intelligence and coordination as well as on tests of oral language skills.

If the physical benefits are not enough to get you off the couch, in 2003 Dacosta and colleagues published a study in the Journal of Psychosomatic Obstetrics and Gynecology showing that mothers who exercised during pregnancy reported less depression, daily hassles, state-anxiety and pregnancy-specific stress while in the first and second trimesters.

GUIDELINES

In 2002 the American College of Obstetricians and Gynecologists (ACOG) issued new guidelines for exercise in pregnancy. The guidelines suggest that in non-complicated pregnancies, women should continue with the general health recommendations of getting 30 minutes of moderate exercise a day for most or all days of the week. This allows the pregnant woman to continue to benefit from healthy levels of activity. Although there is inadequate research on strenuous exercise, athletes who continue to train at a moderate level during an uncomplicated pregnancy are considered safe.

Non-strenuous exercise during the postpartum period has been shown to reduce postpartum depression. Because it is known that weight loss at a moderate pace does not reduce the milk supply, it is safe to resume exercise during the months of breastfeeding.

ACOG recommends women evaluate the risk of injury by contact or falling of any sport they would like to participate in. Most activities are safe, but those posing a risk of abdominal trauma should be avoided. Similarly, scuba diving should be avoided not because of risk for injury, but because the baby's immature circulatory system makes him more susceptible to decompression sickness.

EXERCISE SAFELY

It is considered safe for pregnant women to continue vigorous exercise throughout pregnancy, and women who have not been active are encouraged to begin an exercise regimen during pregnancy. Your health care provider may have information pertaining to your unique situation, so be sure to seek her advice. The following are basic recommendations to help ensure you are exercising safely.

A pregnant woman should be conscious of things that will cause her body temperature to increase. During the first trimester, increased body temperature is associated with neural tube defects. Anytime during pregnancy becoming overheated is uncomfortable and should be avoided. To prevent overheating, be sure to drink plenty of water, wear appropriate clothing and exercise in a properly heated or cooled environment.

The demands on the pregnant body can cause a pregnant woman to fatigue faster while exercising. Pay attention to your body and stop exercising when you get tired, dizzy or short of breath. Remember, you want to maintain your fitness level not make major increases.

Be sure to eat a snack of protein and complex carbohydrates (cheese and wheat crackers, peanut butter on a whole wheat bread) 2 hours before exercising to prevent extreme drops in blood sugar levels.

Avoid breath holding during exertion. Keep your breathing as normal as possible, and exhale during moves that take extra effort.

Avoid positions and exercises that put stress on the stretched abdominal muscles. Also, avoid moves that put extra pressure on your connective tissues of your joints. Your joints will be looser during pregnancy because of the hormone relaxin, and extra care should be taken to ensure you do not damage those joints. Take extra care when adding weights to your routine.

Work out at an intensity that lets you talk during exercise, but not sing. That will let you know you are exercising at a moderate level.

Although exercise can help prevent excessive weight gain during pregnancy, it should not prevent you from gaining a normal amount of weight. The average weight gain for a healthy pregnancy is 35 pounds.

If you are experiencing problems with your pregnancy, talk to your health care provider about how to modify exercises. According to ACOG, a pregnant woman should cease exercising and contact her health care provider if she experiences:

- Vaginal bleeding
- Shortness of breath before exercise
- Headache
- Chest pain
- Muscle weakness
- Calf pain or swelling
- Preterm labor
- Decreased fetal movement
- Amniotic fluid leakage

WHEN EXERCISE IS NOT RECOMMENDED

According to ACOG, there are cases in which it is not safe for the mother to participate in aerobic exercise. The mother is recommended not to exercise if she has:

- Significant heart disease
- Restrictive lung disease
- Incompetent cervix
- Multiple gestation at risk for premature labor
- Persistent second or third trimester bleeding

- Placenta previa after 26 weeks gestation
- Premature labor during the current pregnancy
- Ruptured membranes
- Pregnancy induced hypertension

ACOG also feels in some instances, aerobic exercise may not be safe. Pregnancies should be reviewed carefully if the mother has:

- Severe anemia
- Unevaluated maternal cardiac arrhythmia
- Chronic bronchitis
- Poorly controlled type I diabetes
- Extreme morbid obesity
- Extreme underweight (body mass index < 12)
- History of extremely sedentary lifestyle
- Intrauterine growth restriction in current pregnancy
- Poorly controlled hypertension/preeclampsia
- Orthopedic limitations
- Poorly controlled seizure disorder
- Poorly controlled thyroid disease
- Heavy smoker

The normal healthy pregnant woman will benefit from exercise, so you shouldn't feel concerned about desiring to be active during pregnancy. If at any time you become aware of an issue or concerned about the way your body responds to activity it is appropriate to stop the activity and seek the opinion and suggestions of your midwife.

Chapter Seven
Choosing Exercises

There are three types of exercises that should be part of your overall active lifestyle; aerobic activity, strength training and flexibility training. In addition to your overall healthy activity, it is important to exercise the muscles you will need in late pregnancy and during labor.

AEROBIC ACTIVITY

Aerobic activities are the exercises and sports that use large muscle groups in continuous or rhythmic patterns. These are generally performed at a pace that still allows you to carry on a conversation but do deepen your breathing.

The recommendations for aerobic activity are 30 to 90 minutes per day, three or four days a week. At the beginning of an exercise program, work your way up to 20 minutes a day, and continue to build from there.

Aerobic activities improve the functioning of your heart and circulatory system, increase your endurance and raise your metabolism. They also are helpful at maintaining a healthy weight and improving the way you feel. Most people find regular aerobic activity helps them to feel more energetic.

The most common and easiest aerobic activity is walking. You can do it inside or out, in any weather, it doesn't take any special equipment or expertise and the pace is easy to change when you need to. Other aerobic activities include biking, dancing, using cardio-machines, jogging and using aerobic videos. Choose a variety of activities you enjoy so you won't get bored.

STRENGTHENING EXERCISES

Strengthening exercises are activities that use resistance to train specific muscles or muscle groups. They increase your overall muscle mass which will raise your metabolism, build your bone mass, and tone your body for an overall slimmer appearance.

It is recommended that strengthening exercises be performed on each muscle or group of muscles twice a week, with two days between strength training days. You can divide the work by muscle groups to allow for shorter workouts every day rather than one long full body work out twice a week.

Using your current fitness level and access to equipment as a guide, decide between free weights, weight machines or using your body weight for resistance. Start with a weight that is comfortable for you, but does allow you to fatigue the muscle with the workout. Begin with two sets of 8 repetitions of an exercise, and work your way up to three sets with 12 – 15 repetitions. For a balanced appearance, be sure you train all of your muscle groups.

The most common strengthening exercise is weight lifting. However you can begin to strengthen your muscles without having to invest in expensive equipment. Join a Pilates or yoga class, or purchase a video strengthening program to learn some exercises that will increase your muscle strength with just your body weight for resistance. As your body gets stronger you can purchase hand weights or body bands to increase the resistance and strengthen your muscles even more.

STRETCHING

Stretching movements help prevent muscle soreness after a workout, promote overall muscle relaxation and increases your circulation. Most people find stretching exercises help to make their body feel good.

It is recommended that individuals aim for 30 minutes of stretching three times a week. This can be done in three specific stretching workouts, or by spending time stretching before and after each strength or aerobic workout. Make sure you stretch to the point of comfort, holding each stretch for 10 to 30 seconds while breathing normally.

PREGNANCY EXERCISES

While you are pregnant, the changes in your body can increase the stress on certain muscles and muscle groups, increasing your need to strengthen them. In addition, you may want to begin preparing your body for labor by gaining strength and flexibility in muscles that will be used while giving birth.

Some of this preparation and strengthening can be done by simple changes in the way you hold your body. For example, many pregnant women find their growing abdomen causes them to arch their back which causes lower back aches and weakens the back muscles. By paying special attention to your posture, you can prevent backaches and allow your back muscles to increase in strength as your belly weight grows.

The human pelvis naturally tips forward, and the weight of a growing belly during pregnancy exaggerates this. When the pelvis is misaligned, it shortens the muscles of the lower back and can cause pain. To keep the pelvis in its proper position your deep abdominal muscles have to pull the pelvis up. However, the muscular action that does this is not a "sucking in" of your abdominal muscles. Rather, it is a tucking under of your bottom. You can use the pelvic tilting exercise to help gain control of the muscles for your posture.

You will also want to check your posture while you are sitting. Some chairs encourage poor alignment of your back and pelvis. This may be by allowing slouching, which puts a lot of pressure on the lower back, or by exaggerating the arch of the back. Besides watching your posture, choosing to sit cross-legged when possible gives your back a chance to round and stretch which can help prevent backaches.

Pelvic Tilting

Pelvic tilting can help relieve a sore back by stretching the lower back muscles and is a safe way to keep your stomach muscles toned. It also helps to realign the uterus, and when done before going to bed can help you sleep longer by relieving some of the pressure on your bladder. Pelvic tilting also helps to stimulate the digestive system and can lessen constipation.

While on hands and knees, tilt your pelvis under by contracting deep abdominal muscles. This action will be like tucking your bottom under. While you are learning, try to pay close attention to the abdominal contraction instead of trying to push your back up. This will prevent you from trying to tilt your pelvis by rounding your back. When it is done properly, the movement is very small and your back should stay relatively flat.

Pelvic tilting can be used as part of a regular pregnancy exercise routine, and can also be used throughout the day to prevent a sore back, or when your back begins getting sore. You can start a regular routine of pelvic tilting by doing 50 tilts a day. Work up to 200 a day. They do not need to be done all at once, doing 4 sets of 50 throughout the day is just as helpful.

Squatting

Another exercise for relieving a backache is squatting, which stretches the lower back. Squatting also stretches your calves to help prepare your body for pushing positions when you give birth. Because squatting is the natural position for bowel elimination, it can help lessen the effects of constipation, and squatting to sit can help prevent unnecessary pressure on your pelvic floor.   Squatting to pick up low objects helps prevent excess pressure on your lower back.

Keeping your feet firmly planted on the floor, lower your upper body into a slight bend; lower your bottom to the floor by bending your knees and hips. If you find it is difficult to keep your balance, stand in front of a table, counter, heavy chair or another person, and hold on while you lower your body. You may also try putting your heels on a thick book when you start, and lessening the size of the book as your body becomes more stretched.

To come out of a squat, lift your bottom first, then bring the upper part of your body back into alignment. This helps to prevent putting unnecessary pressure on your knees, which are more prone to injury during pregnancy because of the hormone relaxin.

There is no set standard for how many squats you should do each day. Instead, make squatting part of your every day activities by squatting to pick things up, when talking to small children or to reach low cupboards. As you use squatting during normal activities you will find your flexibility and comfort for squatting will naturally improve. You may also find you are more comfortable keeping a stool in the bathroom to put your feet on and simulate a squat position while you use the toilet.

Pelvic Floor Exercise

The pelvic floor muscles are under tremendous stress during pregnancy. They are responsible for supporting the weight of your growing abdomen and should be strengthened during pregnancy to prevent sagging. Keeping the pelvic floor muscles tone can help prevent urinary incontinence during pregnancy. It also helps keep the vaginal canal tight to prevent damage while the baby passes through during birth.

The pelvic floor exercises are a series of muscle contractions that will take you several weeks to master. Build slowly, allowing yourself at least a week to strengthen and gain control of the muscle. To begin, try to isolate the pelvic floor by contracting it as if you were trying to stop the flow of urine. Do not worry at first about letting go of the muscle contraction, just let it relax on its own. The second step is to learn how to let go of the contraction.

Once you can control the muscle by contracting and relaxing it, begin building the strength of the muscle by holding the contraction for 1 second, then 2 seconds and eventually up to 3 seconds. When you are strong enough to hold the contraction for 3 seconds, increase your control of the muscle by contracting a little, then a little more, then all the way.

The last step is to learn to relax, or bulge the muscle. This is the same movement you use to release the flow of urine. After contracting the muscle, bulge it out (if you have difficultly determining if the muscle is bulged, put your hand along the perineum. You should feel it bulge out as you relax the pelvic floor muscles)

Pelvic floor exercises should be done daily. You can do one long set, however some women find that to be overly tiring for the muscle. It works just as well to do several sets of 10 to 20 contractions throughout the day. Find something you do several times a day, and use that as a reminder to tone your pelvic floor.

Chapter Eight
Prenatal Care

The choices you make during your pregnancy regarding your care will affect the way you experience labor and birth. Understanding the options available to you will help you determine which options are the best for you and your baby. Remember, these are tools God has given you to care for his child inside you. These decisions should be made with great care.

Think of a chain, with each part of your prenatal care as a link in that chain. Your preparations are only as strong as your weakest link. To give you the best chance of staying as healthy as possible and having the best labor experience possible, you will need to build a chain of care with strong links.

LINK ONE: CARE PROVIDER

Unless you live in a very remote area you should have access to a variety of health care providers. Several factors will influence the decisions you make regarding your care.

Listed below are some of the options that may be available to you.

Obstetrician

An obstetrician (OB) is a medical doctor who is a surgical specialist. She is a specialist in the problems of pregnancy. She has access to a wide variety of medical treatments and is able to perform surgery if the need should arise.

Doctor

Other medical doctors are able to provide maternity services for you. Your general physician or family practice physician has access to a variety of medical treatments.

Certified Nurse Midwife

A certified nurse midwife (CNM) has a master's degree in midwifery, which is a specialization in women's health. She is an expert in normal pregnancy and birth, and has training in the problems that arise. She has access to hospitals and a wide variety of medical treatments.

Certified Professional Midwife

A certified professional midwife (CPM) has training in midwifery, but is not a nurse. Her training may have been through a formal educational institution, through an apprenticeship or a combination of both, and she has met the requirements to be certified as a midwife. Depending on the laws where you live she may or may not have access to a hospital.

Direct Entry Midwife

A direct entry midwife, sometimes called a lay midwife, has been trained in midwifery through apprenticeship. In some areas, she may be the only care provider available for home birth.

Keep in mind these are only generalizations about the various abilities of care providers. In some offices you will find that midwives and doctors work together to provide a broad range of care for their clients. Also understand you may not have access to all types of care givers in your community.

Besides the level of care you choose, you will also need to decide what type of care you would like. There are two main models of care in childbirth: the medical model and the midwifery model.

The medical model focuses on what can go wrong and attempts to find and treat any variation from average quickly. Because there are problems with some pregnancies and labors, precautions are taken for every pregnancy and labor regardless of the presence of a problem. Under the medical model, anything outside the average should be treated.

The midwifery model focuses on the normality of pregnancy, and sees it not as a medical condition with potential problems but a healthy time in a woman's life. The midwifery model allows the care provider to treat conditions when they arise, but does not require treatment when a problem does not exist. Furthermore, the midwifery model encourages care for the whole woman; her emotions and family are just as important to her overall health as her physical condition. Under the midwifery model, there is a wide variety of normal on either side of average.

Sometimes the only way to know how a caregiver practices is to see how they react to circumstances that arise during the pregnancy and labor. If you realize the care provider you hired does not give the type of care you desire, remember you are the boss. You hired her and you can fire her at any time.

Once you have chosen the type of care you think is appropriate for you, you can begin to interview care providers. The interview may be the only chance you get to make a decision about the personality, training and birth philosophy of the care giver. You want to be sure you have a list of questions that need more than yes or no answers. The following list may help you develop your own questions. If there is anything on the list that is unfamiliar to you, do a little research before asking the care providers about it.

- In what ways do you support a woman who wants to have an unmedicated labor?
- How much time do you spend with a laboring mother?
- Under what circumstances would you recommend I not attempt an unmedicated, vaginal birth?
- Under what circumstances would you recommend I be induced?
- What are some reasons I might have to labor in bed as opposed to walking around?
- What are some reasons I might need continuous fetal monitoring?
- What indicates to you an IV is necessary during labor?

- What indicates to you an episiotomy is necessary during labor?

- What are the benefits you have seen from squatting for second stage or changing positions during second stage?

- What treatments do you recommend to clients who are diagnosed with gestational diabetes? Or who are group B strep positive?

- What has your experience been with doulas at labors?

Some women investigate their options and decide not to hire a care provider during pregnancy. That is within their rights as a parent. No one can decide for you how much assistance you want or need during your pregnancy. No one, not even the care provider you hire, has the right to force you to do anything during your pregnancy or labor. Making this link of the chain as strong as possible means making the choice that best fits your needs and desires for assistance during pregnancy.

LINK TWO: PRENATAL TESTS

There are a variety of prenatal tests available to you. Basically, a test will give you information to help you make the best decisions possible for the health of you and your baby. For most tests you get to choose if you will have it or not. However there are some tests, such as HIV testing and STD testing, that public health laws make required.

There are two types of tests you will be offered. There are tests that can give you information about your baby's health and well being such as the alpha-fetoprotein test and ultrasound. There are also tests that can give you information about your health and well being, such as the glucose tolerance test and the group B strep test. Your care provider should give you information about every test she is making available to you.

Whether or not you perform a test will depend on your unique situation and the test being offered. Here are some questions to ask yourself as you decide how to handle each test:

- What information will I gain by having this test performed?
- What will I do differently because I have this information?
- Are there any risks to having this test?
- Is it more important to me to have the information or avoid the risks of the test?
- Are there other ways to determine this information?

As with any other health decision you have to make, the choice is yours alone. No one can force you to have a test done, and no one can force you act on the results of a test. Making this link as strong as possible means using tests wisely to determine any changes you may need to make.

LINK THREE: BIRTH PLACE

You may not consider choosing your birth place as a part of your prenatal care, but it is a vital component to strong, healthy birth preparation. As you begin making plans for your labor, you will find that where you give birth will determine what is available to you and may influence the attitude around you when you give birth. Basically, there are three options.

Some women find giving birth at home is the best option for them. Women who give birth at home enjoy the freedom to set the mood and allow the labor to progress without intervention. They also enjoy the comfort and familiarity of the surroundings and those with them. Women who choose not to give birth at home may do so because of a lack of homebirth providers in their area, concern about access to emergency supplies or a lack of interest in the necessary preparations for giving birth at home.

Some women find giving birth at an out of hospital birth center is the best option for them. Women who choose birth centers enjoy the access to emergency supplies and letting the birth center staff handle preparing and cleaning up the birth place. The women who choose this option also enjoy the flexibility a birth center allows when compared to a hospital, and the shorter stays when compared with a hospital. Women who choose not to give birth at a birth center may do so because of the lack of availability in their area or the desire to receive medications not available at a birth center.

Some women find giving birth in a hospital is the best option for them. Women who choose hospitals enjoy the easy availability of emergency supplies and pain relieving medications. The women who choose this option also enjoy letting the hospital staff handle preparing and cleaning up the birth place and the flexibility to remain in the hospital for 24 to 48 hours after giving birth. Women who choose not to give birth at a hospital may do so because of the restrictive policies in some hospitals or the institutional atmosphere that exists.

Do not assume all birth places are the same. There are differences between hospitals in the same city. Take the time to tour the birth places you are interested in, making note of the items most important to you. How supportive is the staff? What options are available to you? Does your prenatal care provider have privileges at that facility? To make this link as strong as possible, you will need to select a birth place that is supportive of your goals for labor.

LINK FOUR: EDUCATION

Your pregnancy, childbirth and lactation educators play a vital role in helping you stay healthy during pregnancy. You can find classes about pregnancy and childbirth at birth centers, hospitals, community centers, pregnancy centers, churches and through independent teachers out of their homes. Classes cover a variety of topics from pregnancy nutrition to caring for a newborn.

Take the time to explore the educational options available in your area. Find classes that fit your goals and beliefs, and give you the skills you need to give birth normally. If possible, talk to the teacher before the class starts to find out if it will actually meet your needs.

In addition to classes, books about pregnancy and childbirth can answer your questions and encourage you to stay healthy. However, some beliefs about pregnancy and childbirth may conflict with your religious beliefs. To make this link as strong as possible, you will need to explore many options to find educational opportunities that help you and your baby stay healthy during pregnancy and prepare you to give birth.

As an issue of stewardship, the prenatal care you receive has the potential to improve your chances for a normal healthy baby and labor experience. The small decisions you make have a snowball effect so they either help you tremendously or hinder you tremendously.

Chapter Nine
Potential Problems

Most pregnancies proceed without problem, with both mother and baby experiencing good health. Your chances of having a healthy pregnancy increase further with good nutrition and exercise. However, an important part of your stewardship of pregnancy is being aware of your overall health and any warning signs of potential problems that may occur.

There are different urgencies with each of the problems listed below. Some signs of a potential problem are just that, indicators that something may need attention but everything may be fine. Other signs of a potential problem are more serious and should cause you to seek the help of your caregiver quickly.

When you are faced with the indicators of a problem, remember to pray for discernment and wisdom in how to handle the issue. "If any of you lacks wisdom, he should ask God, who gives generously to all without finding fault, and it will be given to him" *James 1:5.*

ECTOPIC PREGNANCY

Ectopic pregnancy occurs when the fertilized egg does not travel properly to the uterus. Instead, it implants to the wall of the fallopian tube. This is most common with tubal abnormalities or when the tube has been previously damaged. The fallopian tube is not large enough to hold the growing baby, and so if left untreated the tube can rupture which might result in hemorrhage or even death for the mother. The rates increase with the presence of risk factors, with the highest rates of ectopic pregnancy at around 1-2% of pregnancies.

You may suspect an ectopic pregnancy if during the early weeks of pregnancy you notice a dull or sharp pain in your abdomen that comes suddenly and persists. In some cases the pain may come and go. Other signs that you may be experiencing an ectopic pregnancy are unusual vaginal bleeding, weakness, dizziness or fainting and headaches.

If you suspect an ectopic pregnancy, your caregiver will do a pelvic exam and blood tests to check hormone levels. In an ectopic pregnancy, the levels of hCG increase much slower than during a normal pregnancy. Depending on the results, she may do an ultrasound to help confirm the location of your baby. When an ectopic pregnancy is confirmed, your options will vary depending on how quickly it was discovered.

MISCARRIAGE

When a pregnancy ends on its own before the 20th week it is called a spontaneous abortion or miscarriage. It is estimated that 15 to 20% of all pregnancies end in miscarriage, and the number may be even higher because many miscarriages occur before the mother ever knew she was pregnant.

It is believed that more than half of all miscarriages are the result of chromosomal problems. This does not mean that the parents passed on faulty genes, but as the cells were dividing the chromosomes did not reproduce properly. When this happens, the baby is not able to grow and develop and the pregnancy ends.

Other factors that seem to influence the chances of miscarriage relate to the mother's health, and these seem to occur later in pregnancy. Poor nutrition, smoking, pelvic inflammatory disease, infections, some chronic diseases and abnormalities of the uterus can all play a part in the inability of the mother's body to support a pregnancy.

You may suspect a miscarriage if you experience vaginal bleeding followed by cramping, abdominal pain and a low backache. As many as 25% of all women experience bleeding at some point in pregnancy, of those only about half will actually miscarry. If you have symptoms of a miscarriage, your caregiver will perform a pelvic exam and may do an ultrasound to determine what is happening.

ANEMIA

The increased blood volume during pregnancy increases the need for iron in your diet. If you are not getting enough iron from the foods you eat, you may experience anemia which can cause fatigue, stress and increase your susceptibility for illness. However anemia is unlikely to harm your baby.

You may suspect anemia if you have excessive fatigue and weakness, a pale complexion, shortness of breath, heart palpations, dizziness or light-headedness. Your caregiver may do a test for anemia as part of your standard pre-natal care.

BLADDER INFECTION

Urinary frequency and painful urination are both signs of a bladder infection. Pregnancy increases the chances of having a bladder infection. Although this is not a pregnancy problem, it is important to treat quickly because having a bladder infection increases your risk of preterm labor.

VAGINAL INFECTION

Like a bladder infection, the risks of having a vaginal infection increase with pregnancy. Again, a vaginal infection is not a pregnancy problem but does increase the risk for preterm labor. The normal vaginal discharge during pregnancy is thin and white with a mild odor. If you experience a discharge that is greenish or yellowish, strong-smelling or have redness and itching of the vulva you may have a vaginal infection.

GESTATIONAL DIABETES

Gestation Diabetes is believed to be caused by the changes in the way a woman's body metabolizes foods due to pregnancy hormones. It occurs in about 4% of all pregnancies, and is not usually a threat to the mother's health. Almost half of all women who experience gestational diabetes have no risk factors, and many women have no symptoms. Because of this, the Glucose tolerance Test for gestational diabetes has become a standard for most caregivers.

Although the mother experiencing gestational diabetes may have no symptoms, unless she is monitoring her blood sugar levels the baby may be getting high levels of blood glucose. Elevated blood glucose can cause the baby to develop macrosomia, a condition in which the baby's body is large with the weight particularly distributed through the trunk and shoulders. This large size can make it difficult for the baby to navigate through the pelvis and is associated with shoulder dystocia. At this time, there is no conclusive way to determine the size of the baby before it is born, however it is believed that by following a carefully controlled diet and monitoring blood sugar levels the risks for macrosomia are significantly reduced.

For many women who experience gestational diabetes, changes in eating habits are enough to keep blood sugar levels in healthy ranges. Depending on your test results, your caregiver may recommend that you test your blood sugar periodically throughout the day. In more difficult cases, insulin injections may be suggested.

GROUP B STREP

Group B Strep (or GBS) refers to the bacteria group B streptococcus. About 1/3 of all healthy adults have the group B strep bacteria living in their digestive system, including 10-35% of pregnant women. Because GBS can live in the human body without making the human ill, persons who have the bacteria but show no signs of infection are said to be colonized. A person who is made ill by the bacteria is said to have Group B Strep disease.

GBS is a normal intestinal bacteria and generally causes no problems. However, it is possible for the bacteria to migrate to the vaginal area. This would not make the woman sick, but does make it possible for the baby to come into contact with the bacteria while being born. This contact causes the risk the baby will contract Group B Strep disease during birth.

Many caregivers have made a test for Group B Strep a standard part of their prenatal care services. The presence of the bacteria will make no difference to your pregnancy, but depending on your caregiver, may limit your options during labor.

PREECLAMPSIA

Preeclampsia is a potentially serious condition that can lead to death in the mother or baby if left untreated. There is still much debate about what causes it, however Dr. Tom Brewer has had amazing success at prevention with his pregnancy nutrition program.

Because of the potential seriousness of this disease, caregivers are very careful to monitor for warning signs. You will probably have your blood pressure checked at every visit, and your urine will be checked for protein; both signs of preeclampsia. You should also be aware of any excessive swelling and rapid weight gain which are also warning signs.

The best treatment with preeclampsia is prevention, so be sure to eat well. After the baby is born, the problems from preeclampsia usually go away.

PRETERM LABOR

Labor is preterm if it begins before 37 weeks pregnancy (35 weeks gestation). The main concern is for the health of the baby, who may not be developed enough to live outside his mother yet. In some cases, the mother and caregiver can work together to prevent the baby from being born for a few days or weeks. In others, the baby may need care in a special nursery at the hospital.

For some women, the signs of preterm labor are subtle, usually consisting of uterine contractions. If you experience rhythmic contractions with low back or pelvic pressure, cramps like a menstrual period with or without diarrhea; increase in vaginal discharge, watery discharge or gush of fluid or vaginal bleeding you might suspect preterm labor. Your caregiver will be able to do a pelvic exam to check your cervix for changes, which will then allow you to make decisions about how to proceed.

Part Two
Weekly Guide
to Pregnancy

For you created my inmost being;
you knit me together in my mother's womb.

I praise you because I am
fearfully and wonderfully made;
your works are wonderful, I know that full well.

Psalm 139:13-14

Tracking Your Pregnancy
How to Use of This Guide

WEEK BY WEEK ───────────────────────────────────

The average length of gestation is 266 days, which means your baby will be born around 38 weeks after she was conceived. Because many women are not familiar with their fertility cues and do not know when conception happened, pregnancy is generally measured from the first day of the last menstrual period. By this standard of measuring, your first two weeks of pregnancy happen before your child is conceived. In this guide, the main title for each week is the week of gestation, with the week of pregnancy listed under it.

Please remember babies grow at different rates. The timing given in this guide is for average growth. Some babies develop faster and some develop slower. Also, the growth that happens to your baby is for the most part a long process, with organ systems and body parts taking several weeks to develop and then several more weeks to mature. There is inconsistency with which women experience symptoms of pregnancy; only 50% of pregnant women have morning sickness, one of the most common symptoms.

The differences in pregnancies make it difficult to put together a weekly guide that is accurate for every woman. Even so, this guide can help you understand the basic changes going on in your baby and your body.

DEVOTIONAL ───────────────────────────────────

Each week contains a devotion written specifically for pregnancy. As you read through each week you will be encouraged in your faith and find insights from the Bible to help you stay focused on God during your pregnancy.

PRAYER GUIDE

Each week has a prayer guide to make praying for your baby and your pregnancy easier. The prayer guide has a list of the main changes in mother and baby for each week so you can pray for specific health issues. There are also verses to compliment the devotional so you can pray scripture for the things you are learning. Each prayer guide ends with a short sample prayer based on the devotion. Use the prayer guide as a handy reference for your prayers during the week.

It is my prayer that the reading of this guide will not only encourage you as your pregnancy progresses, but that it will also help you to deepen your relationship with Jesus Christ during this amazing time in your life.

I long to see you so that I may impart to you some spiritual gift to make you strong—that is, that you and I may be mutually encouraged by each other's faith. *Romans 1:11-12*

Before Conception
Pregnancy Weeks 1 and 2

Some of the decisions about your child, such as gender and if he or she will have any chromosomal problems, will be decided at conception, so now, before she is conceived is the time to be praying for a specific gender. Your baby is about to go through the most tremendous physical growth of her entire life over the next few months.

Don't forget about the importance of being as healthy as possible during this exciting time. Be sure you are eating a variety of foods, staying active and getting as much rest as necessary for the healthy functioning of your body. Remember, you and your baby will both be using your body, so it is vitally important to stay as well nourished and rested as possible.

If you are trying to conceive, now is the time you are checking your temperature and vaginal mucus for signs of fertility. Although God gives us cues to help us understand our bodies, whether or not a baby is conceived is always in the hands of God. Don't be overcome with discouragement if it has taken you longer than you expected to conceive, instead take your hurting heart to God who is the only one able to comfort you.

The Feasts
Leviticus 23

Zola Levitt, a messianic Jewish teacher, has found a beautiful correlation between the seven feasts of Israel and the process of gestation. He notes both Passover and ovulation happen on the fourteenth day of the first month. Passover was the day the Spirit of God travel through Egypt killing the first born of the Egyptians, but sparing the Israelites, choosing carefully who would live and who would not. As your body releases an egg, we can only assume God chooses carefully if it will become a child or not.

As we follow the calendar, the next feast is the Feast of Unleavened Bread which is a seven day feast commemorating the sudden traveling of the Israelites starting on the 15th day of the first month. This is the same time frame given for fertilization of the egg in the process of gestation, which happens as the egg is traveling from the ovary into the uterus. This is the beginning, the beginning of the life of your baby and the beginning of the life of the Jewish nation. The other feasts will be mentioned as they occur in pregnancy.

How beautiful that God would draw for us a picture of the gestation of salvation, which was to come from the Jews into the rest of the world. How amazing that when you look at your expanding waistline you can know not only is this baby a gift for you from God, but the very way in which this baby is created, the timeline of his development is a love note from God.

Please see the acknowledgement page in the front of the book for more information about Zola Levitt Ministries, Inc.

Prayer Guide: Before Conception

PRAYING FOR HEALTH

Mom and Dad: *Baby:*
Good nutritional choices   Boy or girl preference
Health
Genetic material

PRAYING THE BIBLE

The fruit of your womb will be blessed, and the crops of your land and the young of your livestock – the calves of your herds and the lambs of your flocks. *Deuteronomy 28:4*

"For I know the plans I have for you," declares the Lord, "plans to prosper you and not to harm you, plans to give you hope and a future." *Jeremiah 29:11*

SAMPLE PRAYER

Lord,

   I come before you humbly asking for your blessing of a child. I know you are in control, and I know you can give me a child. Please give me patience to wait for your timing. Teach me to make good health choices so I can be ready when the time is right. Please keep my body healthy, and bless the fruit of my womb. Please keep my husband healthy as well so our baby has the best start possible.

Amen

Week One
Pregnancy Week 3

If God has blessed you with a child, this week began with the fertilization of an egg. After fertilization, the egg began the process of division which means one cell became two; the two became four and so on. As the egg grows and moves down the fallopian tube into the uterus it secretes a hormone which stops the endometrium (the lining of the uterus) from shedding.

At this point the egg is called a blastocyst and looks like a small ball with a tube forming through the center of it. In some cases, two eggs may be released from the ovary and fertilized which would result in fraternal twins. Sometimes during the initial cell division, the cells completely divide into two unattached cells which would result in identical twins.

Back in the ovary, the corpus luteum (where the egg was) begins producing progesterone which will support the pregnancy by preventing uterine contractions and promoting the growth of blood vessels in the walls of the uterus.

You are probably unsure whether you are pregnant or not. Although your hormone levels have begun to change, it is too early for you to feel any effects of that change. If you have been trying to get pregnant, you may increase your chances by practicing basal temperature and cervical mucus monitoring as part of a natural family planning program.

Be Prepared
Luke 12:35-40

Jesus told the people to be ready for his return using the example of maidens waiting for the bridegroom and being caught off guard by a thief. You have probably never waited by night for the bridegroom to arrive, and hopefully you have never experienced a robbery. So this pregnancy may be your first "prepare and wait" experience.

As you go about the next 9 months growing your baby, making healthy choices and learning about your options for labor you are doing exactly what Jesus recommends in a physical sense. In the excitement (and sometimes frustration) of preparing for a baby it is easy to forget to stay watchful and prepared for the return of Christ.

When you are closer to your baby's expected arrival date, you will understand Jesus' concern even more. There are some things that simply cannot be put off until tomorrow. If labor begins before you have taken the time to prepare, you will most likely struggle and like the owner of the house, wish you had known the time of the arrival so you could be ready.

You will be tired a lot. You will have hundreds of things on your mind. You will need to make decisions and react to all kinds of situations. You will need to learn about the changes you are going through now and will happen down the road. But above all these, you will need to spend time with God preparing your heart and soul not only for the birth of your baby, but also for the return of Christ. As difficult as it may seem to keep up your relationship with God during pregnancy (and believe me, sometimes it is very difficult), it can be done. Not only can you maintain your relationship, you can actually deepen it.

Prayer Guide: Week 1

PRAYING FOR HEALTH

Mom:	*Baby:*
Health	Fertilization
Hormone levels appropriate	Cell division
	Genetic health

PRAYING THE BIBLE

Therefore, prepare your minds for action; be self-controlled; set your hope fully on the grace to be given you when Jesus Christ is revealed. *1 Peter 1:13*

But seek first his kingdom and his righteousness, and all these things will be given to you as well. *Matthew 6:33*

SAMPLE PRAYER

Lord,

Becoming a parent is exciting and scary. Help me be prepared to mother my child. Help me understand the information I find so I can make good decisions and help me to act on the decisions I make. Father, please protect me from becoming over-focused on the pregnancy and my baby to the extent that I would forget to spend time with you. Keep me focused on what is right and good so as I prepare to care for my baby, I will also be continuing to prepare for the return of your son Jesus.

Amen

Week Two
Pregnancy Week 4

Sometime early this week your baby will implant herself into the lining of the uterus (endometrium). When this happens, you may find you have a yellowish discharge from the vagina or spotting. Some women mistake this for a light period. Your baby continues to grow larger while implanting.

As part of the implantation, your baby develops small finger-like projections which will become the placenta. The placenta, along with the ovaries, produce estrogen. Estrogen promotes the growth and changes in your uterus and its lining, the cervix, vagina and breasts. Estrogen also plays a role in insulin production.

The placenta also begins producing hCG (Human Chorionic Gonadotropin), a hormone that prevents the body from rejecting the baby. This is the hormone detected by pregnancy tests, which means you may be able to get a positive reading by the end of this week. For the most accuracy with a test, follow the directions carefully regarding how soon to use it and test with the first urine of the day because it is the most concentrated.

Another hormone secreted by the placenta is hPL (human Placental Lactogen) which alters your metabolism to make sugars and proteins available to nourish your baby. This hormone will also stimulate your mammary glands (breast tissue) to begin developing so they can produce milk. By the end of this week you may begin to feel your breasts are more sensitive or tender to the touch.

The Feast of First Fruits
Leviticus 23

The Feast of the First Fruits could happen on a range of days because it was based on when the Sabbath occurred after the Feast of the Unleavened Bread. This was when the Israelites were to present the first of their harvest to God. In the timeline of gestation this lines up with the implantation of the baby into the uterine lining.

Implantation is the time when the baby begins gaining nourishment from the mother. Before this, the baby was living off the energy stores from the egg, but now the baby is relying on the mother to provide what he needs.

Leviticus 23:14 gives the command; "You must not eat any bread, or roasted or new grain, until the very day you bring this offering to your God." In effect, the Israelites needed to approach God and acknowledge he is the source of their nourishment. How amazing that God reminds the Israelites he is the source of their food at the same place in the gestational timeline the mother becomes the source of food for the baby.

Let the importance of this week's events be a reminder to you about your relationship with God. Are you relying on God as your source of strength? Are you relying on God to provide for your needs? Have you willingly approached God and recognized him as the sustainer of your life?

If you feel led, have your own celebration of the Feast of First Fruits this week. Acknowledge God as the source of your nourishment with a wave offering before a meal, or find a special way to commemorate it between just you and God.

Please see the acknowledgement page in the front of the book for more information about Zola Levitt Ministries, Inc.

Prayer Guide: Week 2

PRAYING FOR HEALTH

Mom: *Baby:*
Health   Implanting in uterus
Proper hormone levels   Growth of the placenta
Breast response   Hormone productions

PRAYING THE BIBLE

I gave you milk, not solid food, for you were not yet ready for it. Indeed, you are still not ready. *1 Corinthians 3:2*

Now he who supplies seed to the sower and bread for food will also supply and increase your store of seed and will enlarge the harvest of your righteousness. *2 Corinthians 9:10*

SAMPLE PRAYER

Lord,

Thank you for this new beginning of life inside me. You are the source of my life, the supplier of my needs. Thank you for reminding me of that this week. Please provide good nourishment for my baby, not only food for the body but also food for the soul.

Continue to supply my needs and the needs of my baby. Keep me healthy so my baby can be healthy. Direct the growth of the placenta so it is strong and able to nourish my baby. As my hormone levels begin to change, please keep me strong and patient.

Amen

Week Three
Pregnancy Week 5

This week, in response to the hormone estrogen, your cervix is changing, your uterine lining thickens and the blood vessels that supply the uterus enlarge so you can nourish your growing baby. By this point the placenta is fully functional and because of this by the end of the week a pregnancy test should return a positive result.

Your body is probably responding to the increased levels of hormones. You may feel an increased tiredness all day, nausea, an increase in urination and may feel bloated. Your breasts should begin to respond with your nipples enlarging and the areolas darkening due to increased blood circulating. You may also begin to notice bumps around the areola (Montgomery's Tubercles) which are glands that produce oils that help to moisturize and soften the skin of the breasts.

Your baby continues to grow and develop. At this point his body is elongating, and a fold of skin along the midline of his body is developing into the neural tube. The neural tube will develop the spinal nerves, cord and brain as well as the backbone. This is the point where your baby is most susceptible to neural tube defects, so be sure to get plenty of folic acid and stay away from excessive heat such as hot tubs.

Your baby's heart is developing along with a primitive circulatory system. By the end of this week your baby's heart will begin beating! For the next few weeks your baby will be at the embryo stage of development.

Rescue Me!
Exodus 5:22-23

When God sends Moses to free his people from Egyptian slavery, instead of Pharaoh letting the people go, he makes their work harder and the Israelites are not even thankful God had sent Moses. Moses cries out to God, "You have not even begun to rescue them!"

Moses couldn't see from God's viewpoint. All he could see was the situation kept getting worse. He was angry and frustrated and not afraid to tell God how badly he felt. God could see more. God could see how this time of suffering would benefit the people of Israel. God knew letting them remain comfortable would mean leaving them prisoners.

Parts of pregnancy and giving birth can be uncomfortable. You may feel frustrated and angry as if God is not helping you. But God knows that to allow you to remain comfortable would bring harm to you and your baby. All the symptoms you are beginning to feel, from the slow and uncomfortable digestion to the fatigue are due to the hormonal changes that need to happen to ensure your baby is able to grow safe and healthy.

If your belly didn't stretch, your baby wouldn't have room to grow. If your breasts didn't respond to the prolactin, you might not be able to nurse your baby. If your uterus didn't contract and your cervix didn't open, your baby wouldn't be able to get out.

Ask God to give you a glimpse of his view. Ask him to help you remain patient through the temporary discomfort and inconveniences so you and your baby can be safe and healthy.

Prayer Guide: Week 3

PRAYING FOR HEALTH

Mom:	*Baby:*
Health	Neural tube development
Comfort	Heart and circulation

PRAYING THE BIBLE

Are not two sparrows sold for a penny? Yet not one of them will fall to the ground apart from the will of your Father. And even the very hairs of your head are all numbered. *Matthew 10:29-30*

And hope does not disappoint us, because God has poured out his love into our hearts by the Holy Spirit, whom he has given us. Romans 5:5

SAMPLE PRAYER

Lord,

I know I am in the father's care. I know you love me and have plans to prosper me. However, I am at a place that makes it difficult for me to see you are still working.

Please help me to recognize you. Please remind me of your love for me. Help me to not only be content with the inconveniences of pregnancy, but also to be joyful about the truth of my body's ability to care for my baby. Please help me to recognize if something becomes unhealthy or more than a normal symptom of pregnancy.

Amen

Week Four
Pregnancy Week 6

Your baby has tripled his size this week, measuring ¼ inch (4-6 mm) from head to bottom, also called crown to rump. Babies are not usually measured head to toe before being born because of the difficulty in measuring the curled up legs.

If you could see your baby now you would see arm and leg buds on the sides of the body, eyes forming on the sides of the head and an opening for the mouth being formed.

Inside your baby the larynx (voice box) and inner ear are developing. Digestive organs such as the liver, pancreas and stomach begin to develop and the lungs begin their long formation process. The neural tube has closed over by the end of this week and the brain is growing in size and developing specific regions similar to an adult brain.

The placenta begins to develop a lining and continues to grow. The umbilical cord also begins to form, separating the baby from the placenta.

Except for some unpleasant side effects from the hormones, the reality of your pregnancy may not have set in yet. Some women fear thinking about the pregnancy until they are sure they will not miscarry. It is impossible to estimate the exact number of pregnancies that end in miscarriage. Some estimate 50% of all pregnancies end in miscarriage before implantation happens. As the pregnancy progresses, the risk for miscarriage decreases. If you experience bleeding, cramping or grayish or pink tissue discharge, contact your caregiver.

God for a Lifetime

"Listen to me, O house of Jacob,
all you who remain of the house of Israel,
you whom I have upheld since you were conceived,
and have carried since your birth.
Even to your old age and gray hairs
I am he, I am he who will sustain you.
I have made you and I will carry you;
I will sustain you and I will rescue you."
Isaiah 46: 3-4

As I read that passage, my heart turns to the line "you whom I have upheld since you were conceived, and have carried since your birth." To know God has been my source of strength and support since my conception is powerful. He will continue to be my support through the entire rest of my life.

But what is even more powerful is to know even now, in these early stages of pregnancy, God is carrying my baby. God is upholding and sustaining the child he is placing in my care, even while she is inside my body. God is her support and her strength.

How freeing to know it is not I, but God who is supplying life to my child. How freeing it is to know I can go to that same God with my needs and he will sustain me as well.

Prayer Guide: Week 4

PRAYING FOR HEALTH

Mom: *Baby:*
Health   Arms and legs
Comfort with symptoms   Eyes and ears
Peace about this pregnancy   Larynx
                                Brain
                                Internal organs
                                Umbilical cord

PRAYING THE BIBLE

"Before I formed you in the womb I knew you.
Before you were born I set you apart;
I appointed you as a prophet to the nations." Jeremiah 1:5

SAMPLE PRAYER

Lord,

My baby is growing and changing so fast. I am so thankful you allowed me to be part of the miracle of one of your children. I know you are the God of my baby now, before he is completely formed. I know you have plans for him, he has a role and a purpose in your kingdom.

Please help me to remember the eternal significance of this child. Teach me what I need to know to help him grow to love you. Help me to see the special gifts you have given to my child.

Amen

Week Five
Pregnancy Week 7

If you could see your baby at this point, you would find the arm and leg buds have lengthened and the arm is divided into a shoulder section and an arm/hand section but there are no fingers yet. Your baby's eyes and nostrils are developing, but the eyes look large and are always open and the nostrils are just nasal pits not a nose yet. His heart bulges out of his chest and the umbilical cord is continuing to lengthen.

Inside your baby, his brain is continuing to develop into separate segments, and the spaces that will hold spinal fluid have formed. His skull is forming, it is still transparent. The lenses of his eyes and his middle ear are forming. His intestinal tract continues to develop, and at this point is too large to fit inside the abdomen so it bulges into the umbilical cord. He even has the beginnings of an appendix and pancreas.

His lungs continue to develop and at this point the main lung passages have been created. Lung development will continue throughout the entire pregnancy. He is about 1/3 of an inch (5-13mm) from crown to rump.

Your body has also developed a mucus plug, a blob of mucus that lodges in the cervix to protect your baby during pregnancy. This will fall out as your cervix dilates in preparation for labor.

At this point you may not have gained any weight, or you may have lost weight due to illness. It is less important to watch your weight than it is to ensure you are eating an adequate diet.

The Comfortable Prisoner

The Israelites said to them, "If only we had died by the Lord's hand in Egypt! There we sat around pots of meat and ate all the food we wanted, but you have brought us out into this desert to starve this entire assembly to death." *Exodus 16:3*

The Israelites were telling Moses it was better to remain a slave in Egypt because they were more comfortable as prisoners then they were in freedom. Slavery was familiar; they knew what was expected of them and what they could expect. Moving to freedom was a challenge, they had to develop new skills and change the way they lived their lives.

Being childless certainly isn't a prison, and parenting isn't freedom, but we can learn a lesson from the difficulty the Israelites had. Every stage of life seems easier when a new challenge approaches. High school is hard while you are there, but when you are in college you look back at high school as having been "easy." It is the same with parenting. Being pregnant seems difficult compared with being childless, but easy compared to caring for a newborn. Mothers with two children look back at having only one child and think, "life was so much simpler then."

You cannot go backwards in life, so you might as well meet the challenge head on. Learn from the example of the Israelites; keep your focus on God. He will take you along the path you need to follow to get to true freedom and a life with blessings beyond your understanding.

Prayer Guide: Week 5

PRAYING FOR HEALTH

Mom: *Baby:*
Health   Arms and legs
Comfort with symptoms   Eyes, ears and nose
Strong cervix and uterus   Lungs
                                   Brain and skull
                                   Internal organs

PRAYING THE BIBLE

In him and through faith in him we may approach God with freedom and confidence. *Ephesians 3:12*

May the God of hope fill you with all joy and peace as you trust in him, so that you may overflow with hope by the power of the Holy Spirit. *Romans 15:13*

SAMPLE PRAYER

Lord,

I come to you knowing what I face is a change for me and at times it will be a struggle. I know you can prepare me, I know you can teach me the things I will need to know. Please let me not get distracted by my fears.

I ask you to help me see clearly the changes that lay ahead so I can be prepared to face them. Let me not be bitter or sorrowful because of what I am giving up. Instead let me be filled with joy for the baby you are giving me.

Amen

Week Six
Pregnancy Week 8

You may be getting frustrated your belly doesn't seem to show any signs of your pregnancy. If this is your first pregnancy you may not begin to show until the 4th or 5th month. Remember, the size of your abdomen is not the size of your uterus. It is growing, and it is displacing your other organs. Right now it is about the size of a grapefruit, still low in the pelvis and putting a lot of pressure on your bladder.

Even though you don't see the growth, your baby is getting bigger every day. By this point she is about ½ inch long (about 14-20 mm) from crown to rump and is big enough that you could see her on an ultrasound. Her arms are growing and have developed elbows and wrists. Her hands and feet look like paddles with little notches which will become fingers and toes. Her trunk is getting longer and straightening out, and she is beginning to develop eyes and ears. Even the tip of her nose is present at this point.

Internally, your baby is continuing to develop organ systems. Her bronchial tubes (main passages of the lungs) are beginning to branch out and her bones may begin to harden (ossification). Her heart rate is about 150 bpm, which is about twice the speed of an adult heart. She is also developing her pituitary gland, and the gonads are developing into ovaries or testes.

You should have scheduled your first pre-natal office visit by now. If you haven't selected a caregiver, get some recommendations from friends and relatives and call to interview the doctors and midwives.

Motivation
Luke 10:25-41

I find it interesting that the story of the Good Samaritan is right before the story of Mary and Martha. The Samaritan showed love for the man by serving him; he was motivated by fulfilling a need. However that same desire to fulfill a need distracted Martha from what she truly needed to be doing.

We can only make guesses as to why Martha's desire to serve her guests distracted her. One possibility is that Martha's motivation for serving her guests was not out of a pure love. Perhaps she prided herself in her ability to host and so it was a selfishness that kept her from sitting with Jesus. It might be she had a grudge against her sister and so was using the preparations as a way to prove she was better, and so bitterness kept her from her guests. She might have been shy, and used the preparations as a way to avoid having to face her fears of being in a group.

As you go about your days preparing for your baby to be born, be sure to look into your own motivation. Does your serving your baby and family display your love, or are you spending so much time preparing that you have been distracted from the things you truly need to be doing?

Prayer Guide: Week 6

PRAYING FOR HEALTH

Mom:
Choosing a care provider
Comfort with symptoms

Baby:
Hands and feet
Testes or ovaries
Lungs
Internal organs

PRAYING THE BIBLE

Praise be to the God and Father of our Lord Jesus Christ! In his great mercy he has given us new birth into a living hope through the resurrection of Jesus Christ from the dead, and into an inheritance that can never perish, spoil or fade – kept in heaven for you. *1 Peter 1:3-4*

SAMPLE PRAYER

Lord,

This child inside me is your child. I am so blessed to have been chosen to care for your child, to serve him until he is able to fulfill your plans for him. I know you have selected the perfect child to help me become the woman you want me to be and I am the perfect mother to help this child become the person you want him to be.

Even now, before I can see or feel my baby, you are loving him and caring for him. Help me to make good decisions for our health and well being. Keep me focused on my baby's needs. Teach me to love him.

Amen

Week Seven
Pregnancy Week 9

Your baby is beginning to look human. His face is rounded and his neck is elongating. His head is still the largest part of his body, and it bends forward so his chin is sitting on his chest. His embryonic tail is disappearing as his body continues to elongate.

His fingers are longer, and feet are forming. His eyelids have grown to almost cover his eyes. He is beginning to move his body and limbs, but because he is so small this movement is only detectable by ultrasound. At this point he is about 1 inch long (22-30 mm).

Internally, digestive organs are forming. The pancreas, bile ducts and gallbladder have formed by this point. The reproductive organs are also forming, but the external genitalia are not developed yet so you will need to wait to guess the sex by ultrasound.

You are nearing the end of the first trimester, but may still be experiencing the common symptoms of nausea, fatigue and dizziness. Your risk for miscarriage decreases as your pregnancy progresses. Only about 15% of pregnancies miscarry. It is thought that more than half of the miscarriages are due to chromosomal abnormalities, and maternal infection may play a part of some miscarriages. It is also known that smoking and drinking alcohol increase the rates of miscarriage. Keep yourself healthy by eating a high quality diet; exercising regularly and getting plenty of rest.

The Feast of Weeks
Leviticus 23

The Feast of Weeks happens 50 days after the Feast of the First Fruits, or 7 weeks which is why it is referred to as the Feast of Weeks. It is the commemoration of Moses bringing the commands of the Lord to the Israelites. Because the Commands of the Lord were their society's laws for government, this feast is a celebration of the nation of Israel becoming a self-governing nation.

In gestation, seven weeks is the time when the baby is recognizable as human. Before this time the baby was not developed enough to be distinguished from other mammals. Once again the feast and gestation mirror each other. The nation of Israel was recognizable as a nation and the baby is recognizable as a baby human.

You might not have given much thought to what your baby looked like before this. Or perhaps you glanced at pictures and thought about how odd the baby looked. What a reminder to us how blind we really are. In the early stages of spiritual growth it can be difficult for us to distinguish what is happening, where we are growing or what the finished product will look like. And sometimes when we get to where we think we need to be, we look back at the start and cannot fathom how we got from there to here.

Thankfully, God has eyes that can see beyond the clearly understood and easily distinguishable. He knows where he is growing us even when we are a bumpy lump of formless flesh. It isn't always pretty to start at the beginning, but the results are well worth it if we let God mold us.

Please see the acknowledgement page in the front of the book for more information about Zola Levitt Ministries, Inc.

Prayer Guide: Week 7

PRAYING FOR HEALTH

Mom:	Baby:
Pregnancy symptoms	Fingers and toes
Peace about baby's health	Testes or ovaries
	Muscles and movement
	Internal organs

PRAYING THE BIBLE

But who are you, O man, to talk back to God? "Shall what is formed say to him who formed it, 'Why did you make me like this?' Does not the potter have the right to make out of the same lump of clay some pottery for noble purposes and some for common use? *Romans 9:20-21*

SAMPLE PRAYER

Lord,

As my child becomes recognizable for the human he is, I am reminded of my growth, how I looked as a spiritual infant. You have grown me so much, and I know I still have so much growth left to go. Thank you for brining me this far, and thank you that you will not leave me here, but will continue to mold me into the woman you want me to be.

Please continue to grow my baby as healthy as possible. Help me to make wise choices in my eating so you have good building blocks. Give me the patience to wait until I am able to feel him move or see my belly start to grow.

Amen

Week Eight
Pregnancy Week 10

At the end of this week the most critical part of your baby's development will be completed and she will officially be called a fetus. Her tail is gone. Her vital organs have been developed and begin to work together. Her bones are formed and becoming solid. Even her ears and eyes have become recognizable. Her eyelids are closed now to allow further development. They will re-open to reveal working eyes sometime between 26 and 27 weeks.

Her upper lip is fully formed, and tooth buds are forming in her gums. She is beginning a time of rapid brain growth, so be sure to continue with good nutrition. If your baby is a boy, his testes are functioning enough to produce testosterone. At this point she is about 1.25 to 1.68 inches (27-35 mm) from crown to rump, and still weighs only .18 oz (5 grams).

Some women begin to feel a thickening in their waist as the abdomen gives way to the growing uterus. You may notice some of your clothes feel tight. Another common experience is of increased emotional sensitivity.

This is the most common week for the first pre-natal visit with your caregiver. Depending on the caregiver you have chosen, you will experience all or some of the following:

Urine Sample
Blood Pressure Monitoring
Weight Check
Pelvic Exam with Pap Smear
Blood drawn for testing
Family History

You Will Not Fall

Even youths grow tired and weary,
and young men stumble and fall;
but those who hope in the Lord will renew their strength.
They will soar on wings like eagles;
they will run and not grow weary,
they will walk and not be faint
Isaiah 40:30, 31

Allow me to share a vision with you. You are holding onto a rope suspended in the sky. Holding is too weak a word; you are clinging to this rope for your life. You are obviously as high as the clouds and the drop, if you let go and fell, would kill you. From somewhere you hear the voice of God saying, "Trust me, let go" and you know you cannot hang on forever, you will have to give up. The most amazing thing happens when you finally let go, you don't fall, not even a centimeter! Instead you float, you fly! It isn't even as if you are suspended or held up by anything, you simply have the strength and power to fly.

God used that image to help me understand it is him who gives me strength, it is he who gives me power and holds me. I waste so much energy and time clinging to the things I do or think I can control to keep me safe. I spend so much time trying to make myself into the person I think God expects me to be. But I don't have to work so hard, because the truth is it isn't me who is able to change me any more than it is me holding myself in the sky (after all, the rope was suspended in mid-air, not tied to anything).

It takes tremendous faith to let go and trust God will take care of you. With a new baby coming, you need to do this now more than ever. Don't try to do it yourself any longer, let go and fly by the power of God.

Prayer Guide: Week 8

PRAYING FOR HEALTH

Mom:	*Baby:*
Intensified emotions	Eyes
Thickening waist	Lips and teeth
Tight clothing	Brain
Medical check-up	

PRAYING THE BIBLE

For the foolishness of God is wiser than man's wisdom, and the weakness of God is stronger than man's strength.
1 Corinthians 1:25

I can do everything through him who gives me strength.
Philippians 4:13

SAMPLE PRAYER

Lord,

My baby is coming soon, and I know he will learn how to rely on you by following my example. Just as important is the fact that when he comes, if I do not allow you to be my strength I will be overwhelmed by the changes and challenges I face.

Help me to see where I am clinging to the things of this world, and give me the strength to let go of them. I know you are my strength, although I don't always know how to rely on you. Teach me to rely on you.

Amen

Week Nine
Pregnancy Week 11

As you move into the second trimester, you may have already gained weight. The average weight gain is 1-2 pounds per month during the first trimester, but you can gain more or less and still be normal. Your uterus is also outgrowing your pelvis, and you may be able to see it sticking out in your lower abdomen.

Your baby has a definite mini-human look, although the head makes up about half of his total length. He is still working on completing his development, with finger-nails appearing this week. As his eyes mature this week they develop the iris. The placental blood vessels increase in size to provide more nutrients to your quickly developing baby.

Although he is only about 1.75 – 2.4 inches (40mm) long, his external genitalia are beginning to form and may be recognizable by ultrasound in the next few weeks. Many caregivers perform an ultrasound at 16 weeks of pregnancy (14 weeks gestation). This allows the baby to be developed enough to determine sex and recognize signs of potential problems, but he is still young enough to use size as a verifier of gestational age.

For many women the second trimester is the most comfortable and enjoyable part of pregnancy. Because your hormone levels are changing again you feel less symptoms of pregnancy. The uterus moves out of the pelvis so it doesn't put as much pressure on the bladder, which can improve your comfort significantly. Many women also find their energy level and libido return during the second trimester.

Heart of a Woman in Labor

Look! An eagle will soar and swoop down,
spreading its wings over Bozrah.
In that day the hearts of Edom's warriors
will be like the heart of a woman in labor.
Jeremiah 49:22

So what exactly is the heart of a woman in labor? You cannot draw too many conclusions about the actual act of laboring from this comparison. God had just promised Edom would be destroyed, and labor does not normally end in death. Besides, God isn't talking about the physical act of war, but about the attitudes, the heart of the warriors.

Like a war turns a boy into a man, labor is the time when the girl dies and the mother is born. The girl is gone forever and cannot comeback. Giving birth is an irreversible and unstoppable force in the life of a woman. She must let go of control and be forever changed. In this comparison, both the warrior and the woman can see what is coming and both know they cannot control what is about to happen.

Both the woman and the warrior may try to fight for control, to try to prevent the inevitable, but eventually they both must concede to the will of God. They both must humbly accept the experience God has chosen for them. They both are forced to recognize it is God who has control, not them. In the end, both have been forever changed.

So what is the heart of a woman in labor? It is a humble heart, accepting the control of God.

Prayer Guide: Week 9

PRAYING FOR HEALTH

Mom:
Symptoms of pregnancy
Increased room for bladder
Increased energy

Baby:
Iris of the eyes
Fingernails
Increasing size

PRAYING THE BIBLE

Humble yourselves before the Lord, and he will lift you up.
James 4:10

Humble yourselves, therefore, under God's mighty hand, that he may lift you up in due time. *1 Peter 5:6*

SAMPLE PRAYER

Lord,

Some days it seems there are so many reasons to be concerned about giving birth. And despite the pain and work that may be involved, the scariest part is I will not have any control over what happens. It is the ultimate test of my trust in you; will I humble myself and not fight the work that needs to be done?

I want to trust you. I want to humbly submit to the work my body needs to do, but I know I am going to need your help to not try to control it myself. Please teach me to relax and allow you to be in control.

Amen

Week Ten
Pregnancy Week 12

Most of your baby's major organs are laid out by this point. They are maturing and beginning to function. For example, her digestive system can absorb glucose and the intestinal muscles can move food through the intestinal system. She naturally swallows amniotic fluid which helps her digestive system get practice. With the digestive system working, she also produces her first urine and eliminates it into the amniotic sac.

There are also major hormonal changes taking place around this time. Her pituitary gland is mature enough to begin producing hormones, and the placenta is mature enough to take over the production of pregnancy hormones. About this time your estrogen levels rise at a faster rate, and they will peak near the end of pregnancy. Your hCG hormone levels are also high which can cause an increased oil production in your skin. This leaves some women with a healthy "glow," while other women find they now have to deal with acne.

As her bones harden and muscles develop, she begins moving her body and limbs. She is still too small to notice the movement, but you may be able to see it on an ultrasound. She can also squint her eyes, open her mouth and move her fingers and toes. She is now about 2.5 inches (63.5 mm) and weighs between ¼ and ½ ounce (8 and 14 grams). If you couldn't hear her heart beat at the first prenatal visit don't worry, it should be audible by the next appointment.

Making Changes

I can feel a significant difference in my body when I am eating healthy and when I am eating junk foods and overeating. When I eat too much or unhealthy my body feels sick, bloated, uncomfortable and slow. When I choose to ignore my hunger I get tired, irritated and can't think clearly. It affects my mood, my reactions to things and my family. But what strikes me is knowing this, knowing how uncomfortable my body gets when I choose foods poorly, I still choose poorly.

Why do I do this? Why do I learn something great and apply it to my life for a short time, only to drop it and end up worse than before? Why do I lack the discipline and perseverance to continue doing the things that benefit me, the things I want to do?

Right now, as you are pregnant and looking forward to the type of parent you want to be, I hope you are making the necessary changes in your life so you can experience the life you desire. But more than simply making the changes, I pray you will persevere through the difficult weeks of making these changes into habits that will continue throughout your entire life.

It is not easy to make changes. It hurts to break old habits and it sometimes takes trying, failing and trying again before you begin to see real progress. Don't give up, it is worth the effort. Through your obedience and humility God will be able to change your heart. It is a slow process, but the only way to really become the mother you want to be.

Prayer Guide: Week 10

PRAYING FOR HEALTH

Mom:
Healthy glow or acne
Increasing estrogen levels

Baby:
Functioning of the organs
Hormone production
Beginning movements

PRAYING THE BIBLE

Therefore, since we are surrounded by such a great cloud of witnesses, let us throw off everything that hinders and the sin that so easily entangles, and let us run with perseverance the race marked out for us. *Hebrews 12:1*

SAMPLE PRAYER

Lord,

I know you are changing me. I know you are showing me so many places I need to work on. Please don't let me get overwhelmed and please don't let me give up. Give me the strength and encouragement I need to keep pressing on even when I fail.

I know you won't remove the obstacles from my path. I know they are there to make me stronger. But please give me eyes to see how to get around these obstacles quickly so I don't keep running into them.

Amen

Week Eleven
Pregnancy Week 13

Congratulations, you have officially begun your second trimester this week. You may find your pregnancy symptoms are decreasing, and you have started to gain some weight. At this point your baby still weighs less than an ounce (13-20 grams) and is around 3 inches (65-78 mm) long. Your placenta, which also weighs about an ounce, has taken over most of the hormone production, and is producing progesterone and estriol.

Your baby's face begins to look more human now, as the face widens to allow the eyes to face the front rather than the sides. He may begin putting his thumb in his mouth as the sucking muscles begin developing. He is also beginning to form skull bones, although these bones are not hardening yet.

Your baby's body continues to elongate which gives his trunk enough room to hold the intestines which have been pushed into the umbilical cord as they developed due to a lack of space. His digestive system continues to mature. His intestinal villi (which move food through the system) are forming and his pancreas begins secreting insulin.

If you have an ultrasound at this point, you may be able to see a few ribs. You may also be able to tell if you are going to have a boy or girl, if baby is in the mood to cooperate.

Fear and Courage

Courage is contagious. I can catch it from others and I can pass it on to others.

Fear is contagious too. I remember being a little girl and afraid of the woods behind our house. I don't know if my brother was frightened, but I knew if he went with me I could walk in the woods. I never acted scared, just as calm and confident and as natural as a scared 10 year old could because I knew even at that young age if I told him I was scared, it would increase any fear he had. My big fear was finding out he was afraid too, because I just knew if he was afraid I wouldn't be able to overcome my fears and walk in the woods with him any more.

As you prepare for labor and parenting, you are being exposed to many people's thoughts, philosophies and concerns. Most of the advice is unsolicited and comes from well meaning friends and even strangers who hope to impart you with some wisdom. Yet, you may be catching more than a few good hints about how to handle labor. Are you catching courage or are you catching fear? How are you really affected by the comments made to you?

What about the comments you make? When you speak to other women about your experience this far and your thoughts about the future, what do you say? Are you passing on courage or are you passing on fear?

Prayer Guide: Week 11

PRAYING FOR HEALTH

Mom:
Gain and give courage

Baby:
Proper placental functioning
Facial changes
Thumb sucking
Maturing digestive system

PRAYING THE BIBLE

Therefore encourage one another and build each other up, just as in fact you are doing. *1 Thessalonians 5:11*

May our Lord Jesus Christ himself and God our Father, who loved us and by his grace gave us eternal encouragement and good hope, encourage your hearts and strengthen you in every good deed and word. *2 Thessalonians 2:16-17*

SAMPLE PRAYER

Lord,

You say the tongue is like a fire or the rudder of a ship in the way it affects the body. I don't want to spread fear anymore. I don't want to catch the fears of others. I want to be an encourager, and to be encouraged by the conversations I have.

Father, please make me aware of the words I listen to or speak that spread fear about labor, giving birth and becoming a mother. Teach me to spread courage and hope instead of fear and panic.

Amen

Week Twelve
Pregnancy Week 14

You may begin to notice some skin changes around this week. The linea nigra is a dark line that can form from your navel to your pubic bone. You may also find your areolas and nipples have gotten darker and larger. Some women need to begin wearing larger clothing, or clothing made specifically for a growing belly this week.

Physically, your baby is continuing to become increasingly "human" looking. Her head and neck are elongating, which makes the ears look like they are moving up into their proper place. She is growing hair on her head and eyebrows, as well as a special hair on her body called lanugo that will help protect her skin from the amniotic fluid.

Her thyroid gland has matured and is now able to produce hormones. The digestive system is mature enough to produce and eliminate urine into the amniotic fluid. Not only does she drink the amniotic fluid, but practices breathing it too.

With all the organ systems in place and maturing, her body starts warming up the nervous system and muscles. As her muscles continue to develop, the nerves that will control the muscles are also laid down and signals sent to start exercising the muscles. At only about 3.5 – 4 inches (80-100 mm), she is still too small for you to feel these movements.

A Sabbath of Rest

In Exodus 35 God gives us the principle of taking a day off each week. The idea of the Sabbath is that you do no work, instead focus on growing closer to God and presumably family and close friends.

I am a stay-at-home mom. I have no responsibility outside my home and family unless I choose to. Yet I still find the idea of a Sabbath overwhelming. My first reaction is it cannot be done, I have too much important stuff to do to take a day off. When I begin to feel this way I realize how far from God my priorities have strayed.

My family can eat easy-to-prepare foods or even leftovers (which I personally detest) one day a week. I can go one day without needing to put in a load of laundry. I can easily use disposable dishes to stay away from extra kitchen work.

Yet, I still find that to discipline myself to have a Sabbath each week is more difficult than it should be. I have made so many unimportant things more important than God and more important than my family. Sure errands need to be run, and the house needs to be clean, but it doesn't need to be done every day.

What is on your list? What things do you make more important than God and your family? What things are keeping you from spending time with God as you let one of his children grow inside you?

Prayer Guide: Week 12

PRAYING FOR HEALTH

Mom: *Baby:*
Changing body shape   Growth of hair
Skin coloration changes   Thyroid gland
                                Nervous system

PRAYING THE BIBLE

Come to me, all you who are weary and burdened, and I will give you rest. Take my yoke upon you and learn from me, for I am gentle and humble in heart, and you will find rest for your souls. *Matthew 11:28-29*

There remains, then, a Sabbath-rest for the people of God; for anyone who enters God's rest also rests from his own work, just as God did from his. Let us, therefore, make every effort to enter that rest, so that no one will fall by following their example of disobedience. *Hebrews 4:9-11*

SAMPLE PRAYER

Lord,

A Sabbath rest seems impossible most of the time. And yet I know you call me to take a day to reflect on you each week. Help me trust you enough to let go of all the things I think are important.

As I learn to celebrate a Sabbath, help me to recognize the unimportant things I cling to as important. Show me the things I let get in the way of my family. Help me to make the right choices, and to give things their proper priority.

Amen

Week Thirteen
Pregnancy Week 15

You should be able to feel the top of your uterus (fundus) about 3 or 4 inches (75-100 mm) below your belly-button now, but that is not the only growth you've experienced. Your heart is pumping 20% more blood now than before you were pregnant. By the end of your pregnancy it will have increased 30-50%. This added strain on your heart may cause you to feel fatigued sooner than you normally would during exercise or exertion. Some women also complain of feeling "scatterbrained" by this point in pregnancy.

Your baby is continuing to mature. The hardening of his bones is happening very quickly by now. If you were to have an X-ray done (which is not recommended because it can cause damage to your baby), you would be able to see his skeleton. If you were able to see your baby, his skin would be translucent, allowing you to see blood vessels underneath it.

His eyes and ears are almost in position now. If he will have dark hair, hair follicles may begin to make the pigment. As his hair comes in, a scalp hair pattern is developing. His bones and muscles continue to mature, and he is developing new skills. By now he can make a fist. He can also bend his arms at the wrist and elbow. He is about 4.1 – 4.5 inches (93-103 mm) and weighs about 1.75 ounces (70 g)

You may need to make decisions about several prenatal tests now. You may be offered the Triple Screen or an amniocentesis. Take your time in making a decision. Educate yourself to ensure that the benefits of this information outweigh any risks they may have in your situation.

Freedom and Opportunity

One thing I frequently hear is "I'm not taking a childbirth class or reading any books because I want to be free to do what feels right for me during labor." I always get a little concerned when I hear this because it shows a lack of understanding of the difference between freedom and opportunity.

In labor, you may have the opportunity to use a variety of tools and comfort measures to help you manage the stress and discomforts of your labor. Depending on the birth place you have chosen, you may have a wide variety of options, or only a few things may be available to you. You may also find your health or other circumstances limit your opportunities.

Freedom however, is not just the availability of an opportunity. Freedom exists when you are able to take advantage of an opportunity. Regardless of how many or how few opportunities you have, without preparation you are not able to act on any opportunity, and so you have no freedom. If you are not familiar with your options, you have no options. If you have not taken the time to learn a skill, it is not a skill you will be able to use in labor.

For true freedom in labor you must understand the basic labor process, and how you can help or hinder that process. You should be familiar with a variety of ways to cope with the pain, discomfort and fatigue you may feel. Then, when the opportunity to use the skills arrives, you will have the freedom to use whichever is most appropriate.

Prayer Guide: Week 13

PRAYING FOR HEALTH

Mom: *Baby:*
Increased blood volume   Hardening of the bones
Feeling 'scatterbrained'   Coordination of movements
Decisions for prenatal tests

PRAYING THE BIBLE

Be very careful, then, how you live—not as unwise but as wise, making the most of every opportunity, because the days are evil. *Ephesians 5:15-16*

SAMPLE PRAYER

Lord,

I know if I am not able to work with the tools you give me, then I become a slave to my lack of preparation. Help me to see clearly how much work I need to do to be ready to make the most of the opportunities you give me for the rest of this pregnancy and during the labor.

At the same time God, please give me the wisdom to know when enough is enough. Don't allow me to become obsessed so I spend all my time preparing for labor. Help me to have the right perspective so I will have freedom in my pregnancy and during labor.

Amen

Week Fourteen
Pregnancy Week 16

Your baby is not quite 5 inches (about 16 cm) yet, but an experienced mother may be able to begin recognizing the feelings of movement as she exercises her muscles. First time mothers may need to wait a few more weeks before they are certain they are feeling movement.

Another exciting milestone is the external genitalia are sufficiently developed to allow at least a 75% accurate guess at the sex of your baby with ultrasound. You do not need to discover the sex during an ultrasound; some families prefer to keep it a surprise. In some instances babies adopt postures and positions that keep the sex a secret from frustrated parents.

Your baby is beginning to gain control of her muscle movements. She can even make facial expressions in response to changes in the uterine environment.

As her body continues to lengthen, the umbilical cord seems to migrate down her abdomen. Her legs are now longer than her arms. She is also forming her finger and toe nails. If you are having a girl, her ova (eggs that will become her future children) are beginning development now.

Your larger uterus has moved out of your pelvis and into your abdomen which may decrease the frequency of urination you felt during the first trimester. However, your baby urinates every 40-45 minutes now.

Struggling
Romans 7:15

Have you noticed you have changed since becoming pregnant? Do you feel like you are lost or struggling some days? Perhaps you suddenly feel lazy or quick-tempered even though it has not been a part of your nature before. Romans 7:15 tells us "I do not understand what I do. For what I want to do I do not do, but what I hate I do."

Even Paul shouted, "What a wretched man I am! Who will rescue me from this body of death?" (Romans 7:24) And yet he continued on to tell us there is no condemnation for those who are in Christ Jesus. He gives us three useful pieces of information to help us with this struggle.

First, set your mind on what the Spirit desires. Don't allow your thoughts to dwell in sin, catch them and change what you are thinking about. You can focus your thoughts on what is good and right.

Secondly, remember what you are struggling with now is not able to compare with the glory that will be in you when you are complete.

The most important point to remember is this: the Holy Spirit will help you in your weakness. Yes you are weak, but you are not alone. Yes, you may struggle but you do not have to struggle of your own strength. Yes, this is difficult, but God has not abandoned you. In fact, God is using this time of change in your life to further refine your heart so you will be the woman he designed you to be.

Prayer Guide: Week 14

PRAYING FOR HEALTH

Mom:
First feelings of movement
Constant need to urinate

Baby:
Determining the sex of baby
Increasing muscle control
Ova (eggs) for a girl

PRAYING THE BIBLE

In the same way, the Spirit helps us in our weakness. We do not know what we ought to pray for, but the Spirit himself intercedes for us with groans that words cannot express. *Romans 8:26*

Finally, brothers, whatever is true, whatever is noble, whatever is right, whatever is pure, whatever is lovely, whatever is admirable—if anything is excellent or praiseworthy—think about such things. *Philippians 4:8*

SAMPLE PRAYER

Lord,

It gets so frustrating when I just don't feel like myself. I feel so weak sometimes, as if I couldn't be patient or loving if I tried. But I know you are my strength in weakness. I know you will support me and uphold me even when I feel I'm doing everything wrong.

Please keep me focused on what is right. Don't let me dwell on the negative or allow my mind to stay in the sin. When my thoughts are wrong, let me see it right away and help me change my attitude.

Amen

Week Fifteen
Pregnancy Week 17

You may be reassured to know that a 5 to 10 pound weight gain at this point is normal. It is also normal to sweat more and have an increase in nasal and vaginal discharge because of the increased fluids in your body.

You may be able to feel the top of your uterus about 2 inches (50 mm) below your navel (about half-way from your pubic bone to your navel). As your baby grows, the uterus grows in an oval shape rather than round to accommodate him. This means that it will get taller than it gets wide.

Your baby is still not quite 5 inches long (110 – 120 mm), but at about 3.5 ounces (100 g) he finally weighs more than the placenta. The placenta will continue to grow throughout the pregnancy to meet your baby's increasing demands for oxygen, nutrients and elimination of waste. At this point, the placenta is about 1 (25 mm) inch thick.

To help your baby maintain proper body temperature, he is developing a special type of fat called brown fat. It will make up about 2.5% of his weight at birth, and will slowly go away after he is born.

The bones of his inner ear are forming and hardening, which means he will soon be able to hear noise. Some mothers find their baby responds to loud or sudden noises now, however to know if this is happening you would need to have felt the baby move.

Preparation

A man's riches may ransom his life,
but a poor man hears no threat.
Proverbs 13:8

It is certainly a valuable principle to be prepared for what might happen. Yet, sometimes in our preparations we become more concerned about what might happen then we are with what is really going on around us. This is certainly true during pregnancy and giving birth.

We are bombarded with messages telling us there is great danger if we don't eat these foods, prepare with these books and do exactly as we are told. As we struggle to meet the expectations of those around us, we are left frustrated, frightened and forgetting the importance of what is about to happen. And the irony is, the more prepared we are for the unexpected problem, the more likely we seem to be to have a problem.

And yet, we cannot allow ourselves to stick our heads in the sand and just blindly hope for the best. As the mother of your child, God has given you the responsibility to do your best to ensure the health and safety of his child. You must make choices that will support the health and well-being of your child and this means you must purpose to spend some time preparing for what is ahead.

I wouldn't suggest you not prepare for what is coming. However, I also wouldn't suggest to be prepared for absolutely every possibility because I know some preparations can make you vulnerable to the problems they are designed to help. I would recommend you do your best to honor God through good stewardship and trust he will give you the strength to handle any challenges that may come.

Prayer Guide: Week 15

PRAYING FOR HEALTH

Mom: *Baby:*
Appropriate weight gain   Healthy placenta
Increased bodily fluids   Brown fat deposits
                                Development of hearing

PRAYING THE BIBLE

May the God of hope fill you with all joy and peace as you trust in him, so that you may overflow with hope by the power of the Holy Spirit. *Romans 15:13*

We live by faith, not by sight. *2 Corinthians 5:7*

For the foolishness of God is wiser than man's wisdom, and the weakness of God is stronger than man's strength.
1 Corinthians 1:25

SAMPLE PRAYER

Lord,

I know I need to prepare, but it becomes so easy to allow myself to spend all my time studying everything about pregnancy and birth. I am sometimes tempted to put my trust in my own wisdom and understanding than in your strength and care.

Help me to be wise in my preparations for giving birth and becoming a mother. Don't allow me to be a fool who does not prepare for what lies ahead, but don't let me be a fool who works for what is unnecessary. Help me trust in you.

Amen

Week Sixteen
Pregnancy Week 18

Your baby is continuing to mature. Her finger prints have developed, and she is now swallowing up to a liter of amniotic fluid a day. She is about 5.5 inches (12.5 – 14 cm) long and weighs about 5.25 ounces (150 g). She is developed enough that an ultrasound at this point can detect some heart abnormalities.

Her face has a baby-like appearance. Her eyes and ears are in place, and the hair on her head and eyebrows is starting to appear.

Two exciting things happen around this week: your baby may be developed enough to see and to hear. Your baby uses these skills before she is born as a way to familiarize herself with the environment she will live in. Although her eyes are only able to detect the difference between bright light and darkness, this helps her learn about the day/night schedule where you live.

The sounds she hears are muffled because of the amniotic fluid, but she does hear enough to become familiar with the voice of her mother and others who live in her home. She may also become familiar with the type of music you listen to.

Some families enjoy using these skills to begin bonding with their baby. You can use a flashlight to shine light on the belly, and your baby may turn to see what it is. You can listen to music with your baby, read her stories or just talk to her. If you have a toy that makes a sound, you can use that sound to signal the beginning of a play time for your baby by playing it on your belly before you begin talking, singing or rubbing your belly.

Relationships with Authority
Romans 13:1-2

God has called us to submit to the governing authorities he placed over us because to rebel against them is rebelling against God himself. For most of our lives this principle has carried over to other figures of authority. We submit to our teachers, our employers and our medical authorities. However, it is important to understand there is a difference between a governing authority and a medical authority.

Your doctor or midwife is not in a position of authority over you. The type of authority they are is more similar to being an expert. In fact, you are in a position of authority over your caregiver because you are the employer and she is the one hired. The relationship should allow you the time you need to ask questions and get answers. Think of your caregiver like a consultant you hire to give you information you cannot get on your own. It is still your right and responsibility to make the decision for how you will proceed at every step of your pregnancy and your baby's birth.

Realizing the responsibility you have for making decisions may change the way you think about your role in this pregnancy. Perhaps you have been dissatisfied with the care you received from your caregiver but thought there was nothing you could do. You have the freedom to hire any doctor or midwife you choose, you may not be able to have your insurance cover the fees, but you do have that freedom. Perhaps you have deferred all decision making to your caregiver thinking it was her responsibility to keep you healthy. That is an unfair expectation of your caregiver because the ultimate responsibility for what you choose to do with your health is yours.

Do you need to reevaluate your relationship with your care provider and make some changes in the way you manage your health?

Prayer Guide: Week 16

PRAYING FOR HEALTH

Mom: *Baby:*
Bonding with baby   Vision
                                Hearing

PRAYING THE BIBLE

And masters, treat your slaves in the same way. Do not threaten them, since you know that he who is both their Master and yours is in heaven, and there is no favoritism with him. *Ephesians 6:9*

Be wise in the way you act toward outsiders; make the most of every opportunity. Let your conversation be always full of grace, seasoned with salt, so that you may know how to answer everyone. *Colossians 4:5-6*

SAMPLE PRAYER

Lord,

Relationships are hard enough between friends, when someone is hired to offer advice and expertise the relationship can become muddled. Help me to understand how to keep a right relationship with my doctor/midwife. Don't allow me to mistreat her, but don't allow me to expect too much of her either.

If she is not a Christian, help me to be a light shining your love. Help me to be confident in the responsibilities you have given me, and don't allow me to be weak about requesting what I know is right. If there is someone who I can work with better, please show her to me.

Amen

Week Seventeen
Pregnancy Week 19

If you haven't felt it yet, this may be the week you first feel your baby's movements. His motor neurons (nerves that send a signal from the brain for the muscle to move) are continuing to develop. This allows him to make more deliberate, conscious movements. As his control over his muscles improves, you can "play" with him by rubbing or gently poking your belly. He will probably respond by moving or kicking.

Your baby has been developing two forms of protection for his skin; lanugo hair and vernix caseosa. The vernix is a thick and creamy white substance that prevents the amniotic fluid from damaging the skin. It slowly wears off near the end of your pregnancy, so babies born early tend to have more on their skin than babies born late. Lanugo hair develops all over the body and seems to help the vernix remain attached to the skin. The lanugo will also fall off near the end of your pregnancy.

He is also developing the tooth buds that will become his permanent teeth. These are in his gums behind the milk teeth buds. If your baby is a girl, her ovaries now hold primitive egg cells.

It is easy to be lulled into thinking nothing important is happening with your baby now because there are no new body systems being developed at this time. However, the maturation of all his body's organs, tissues and systems is in full force. It is still important for you to eat well and get plenty of rest to nourish you and your baby.

Special Messages from God

Therefore we do not lose heart. Though outwardly we are wasting away, yet inwardly we are being renewed day by day. For our light and momentary troubles are achieving for us an eternal glory that far outweighs them all. So we fix our eyes not on what is seen, but on what is unseen. For what is seen is temporary, but what is unseen is eternal.
2 Corinthians 4:16-18

I am a firm believer that the Bible has relevance to my life right now. I am also a firm believer that something must be written down or I will forget it. I have several Bibles that are marked up, underlined and filled with notes in all the margins because God was speaking so clearly to me when I read.

I found the following note about the above passage in the margin of my Bible I read while pregnant with my son. Some may consider it inappropriate to change scripture, but I think of it as translating it to a language I can better understanding:

Don't lose heart! My figure may be dying but I am more alive every day. My body is growing to build a baby who houses an eternal soul. So don't think about the hips and the waistline, instead think of the baby. The changes in my body are temporary, my baby is eternal.

Praise God the Bible can speak to us about anything we are going through. What is God saying to you about your pregnancy from your daily Bible reading?

Prayer Guide: Week 17

PRAYING FOR HEALTH

Mom:
Playing with baby
Feeling baby move

Baby:
Development of nerves
Lanugo hair and vernix
Development of tooth buds
Maturation of body

PRAYING THE BIBLE

For the word of God is living and active. Sharper than any double-edged sword, it penetrates even to dividing soul and spirit, joints and marrow; it judges the thoughts and attitudes of the heart. *Hebrews 4:12*

All Scripture is God-breathed and is useful for teaching, rebuking, correcting and training in righteousness, so that the man of God may be thoroughly equipped for every good work.
2 Timothy 3:16-17

SAMPLE PRAYER

Lord,

Please open my eyes to all the treasures awaiting me in your word. Help me to see special messages just for me during this pregnancy.

I trust your perfect timing. I know what I read from the Bible is not by chance. You are trying to help me grow. Please help me to recognize how I am growing through reading your word. Thank you that the Bible is still relevant to my life today.

Amen

Week Eighteen
Pregnancy Week 20

At this point your baby is between 5.6 − 6.4 inches (14-16 cm) and between 9 and 10 ounces (260 g) in weight. Her skin is developing the layers it needs to provide protection to the bones, muscles and other tissues underneath. This thickening process will make her skin opaque (you will not be able to see through it any more).

Your uterus has grown, and is about even with your navel now. As it continues to grow, you will feel pressure on your lungs, stomach, bladder and kidneys. You may find it hard to take a deep breath, and you may need to adjust your meal times so you eat smaller meals more often.

For some women, the stretching of the abdomen causes itchy skin. Be sure to apply a moisturizer to keep the skin soft and to prevent it from drying out (which may make the itching worse).

The pressure of the uterus may also cause diastasis recti a separation of the connective tissue between the long strap muscles of the abdomen. This is not dangerous and will repair itself after your baby is born.

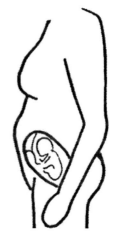

Congratulations, you are half-way through your pregnancy! Although it seems to be taking forever, your baby will be here before you know it.

Being Yourself

It is a beautiful thought for me to go back to my teenage journals and understand how so much of who I am is wrapped up in the words on those pages. Writing has always slowed down my thoughts and forced me to truly understand what problem I was facing. But it wasn't until I was an adult that I realized my journals were really just me talking to God.

Its funny, I kept trying to get rid of the writing so I could be more intimate with God by having more prayer time. I had set in my mind an idea of the perfect relationship with God, and did my best to make that relationship a reality. Yet instead of drawing me closer to God it left me more frustrated and spiritually exhausted. I can only imagine how God felt as he watched me struggle to try to be someone he did not make me to be, and how full of joy he must have been the day I finally realized it was ok to write out my prayers.

When you are pregnant, a lot of people will give you advice and tell you how you "should" be doing things. For the most part these suggestions are harmless and come from a real concern for you and your baby. But before you begin to conform to an image you have created of the perfect mother, let me encourage you to make sure the person you strive to be is the person God made you to be, not some society standard of the perfect mother.

Prayer Guide: Week 18

PRAYING FOR HEALTH

Mom:
Adjusting to growing belly
Itchy skin
Patience for pregnancy

Baby:
Thickening of skin
Healthy growth

PRAYING THE BIBLE

Remember your leaders, who spoke the word of God to you. Consider the outcome of their way of life and imitate their faith. Jesus Christ is the same yesterday and today and forever. *Hebrews 13:7-8*

Follow my example, as I follow the example of Christ. *1 Corinthians 11:1*

SAMPLE PRAYER

Lord,

I am pulled in so many directions, and some days it seems everyone has a different idea of who I should be. Please help me to stay focused on you, knowing all I need to do is be an imitator of Christ.

Help me learn from the examples of those around me, but don't allow me to begin to idolize them. And let me become an example for the women who become pregnant after me. However, let me be an example for them to be more like Christ, not to be more like me.

Amen

Week Nineteen
Pregnancy Week 21

Now that your baby is able to turn and move freely and is just over 7 inches (18 cm) from crown to rump, you should be feeling movements. Some women describe it as "bubbles" or "fluttering" low in the abdomen. It is still a small feeling because your baby only weighs about 10.5 oz (300 g) yet.

As the bones are hardening, the bone marrow is also developing. It is now developing the ability to produce blood cells (this is the function of marrow in an adult). Until the marrow can do this on its own, your baby's liver and spleen are making his blood. Although the placenta allows him to get nutrients and oxygen from your blood, his blood never actually comes into contact with your blood and he does have his own blood supply.

His digestive system is developed enough that he has begun digesting the amniotic fluid he swallows. It is unclear if the absorbing of the fluid by the intestines is helping the system develop properly, or if it actually provides essential nutrients for him.

One of the side-effects of swallowing amniotic fluid is a build-up of the undigested debris in the colon. This material, called meconium, will be your baby's first bowel movements.

You may find your legs and feet get swollen at times. You may also find your posture changing to accommodate the growing uterus. Try to keep your back straight rather than arched to help prevent backaches. You can practice this by standing against a wall.

A Woman in Labor

As a woman with child and about to give birth
writhes and cries out in her pain,
so were we in your presence, O Lord.
We were with child, we writhed in pain,
but we gave birth to wind.
We have not brought salvation to the earth;
we have not given birth to people of the world.
                    Isaiah 26:17-18

The verses about laboring women in the prophets can be intimidating. God seems to use the image of a woman in labor as a metaphor for fear, trembling and pain. Sometimes it makes me want to yell, "Come on God! Give me some hope here; I have to go through this you know." Sometimes I just ignore the verses.

We don't have to ignore these verses, and we don't have to dread labor because of them. For example, this passage from Isaiah compares the Israelites to a woman in labor. If you read the passages before it you will discover that Isaiah is talking about the experience the Israelites will have when God completes his promise and brings salvation to the whole earth through Israel.

Isaiah explains there were other gods, and they fell before the one true God. He then uses the birth analogy to show how Israel tried to bring salvation to the people of the world, but they were not able to do it. He says it is only God who could bring salvation.

A woman about to give birth feels her labor and calls out to God for his help to give her strength and to bring forth her child. Isaiah shows us that although a woman can give physical birth to a child, it is only God who can give spiritual birth to people. The glory in both "labors" is the fact it is God who brings forth life, not our efforts.

Prayer Guide: Week 19

PRAYING FOR HEALTH

Mom:
Feeling the baby move
Swelling of feet and legs
Posture

Baby:
Marrow of the bone
Digestive process

PRAYING THE BIBLE

But when the kindness and love of God our Savior appeared, he saved us, not because of righteous things we had done, but because of his mercy. He saved us through the washing of rebirth and renewal by the Holy Spirit, whom he poured out on us generously through Jesus Christ our Savior. *Titus 3:4-6*

For you have been born again, not of perishable seed, but of imperishable, through the living and enduring word of God.
1 Peter 1:23

SAMPLE PRAYER

Lord,

Help me to be understanding of the way you talk about giving birth in the Bible. Don't allow me to become discouraged or fearful because of your comparisons. Help me to have faith in you, to trust you even with this part of my life.

As I work towards giving birth, help me remember to call on you. Let this physical birth be a reminder to me of the spiritual birth that is necessary to live with you and the gift of life you have given to me.

Amen

Week Twenty
Pregnancy Week 22

Your baby is working on developing two more senses, taste and touch. All her organ systems are in place, but the specialization and maturation of the systems is continuing. If your baby is a girl, her reproductive organs have formed and are in the proper place. If your baby is a boy, his testes are beginning the descent from the abdomen to their proper place in the scrotum.

Her kidneys are developed enough now that they are beginning to make real urine which is excreted into the amniotic fluid. Before this, the fluid was moved through the body but not processed in this way by the kidneys.

Experienced mothers may begin feeling Braxton-Hicks contractions. These are normal contractions of the uterus which help to strengthen the uterine muscle in the same way a bicep curl would help to strengthen the bicep muscle. Most women find these to be painless, some don't even realize they are having them unless they happen to touch their belly and it is very hard.

If you are still experiencing fatigue, you may be suffering from anemia. Anemia is a condition in which there are not enough red blood cells to provide the necessary amounts of oxygen. Your caregiver can determine if this is a problem with a blood test. Treatment may be as easy as making small changes to your diet or by taking an iron supplement.

At this point your baby is about 7.5 inches (19 cm) from crown to rump, and weighs just under a pound (350 g).

True Peace during Labor

Jesus called the crowd to him and said, "Listen and understand. What goes into a man's mouth does not make him 'unclean,' but what comes out of his mouth, that is what makes him 'unclean.' *Matthew 15:10-11*

Jesus was very clear about telling us it is not what goes into a person that makes her unclean, but what comes out of her. That is because what comes out of the mouth comes from the heart. Spend some time examining your heart, and be honest about what you see. This is the heart you will have with you while you labor.

You cannot "prepare" for a peaceful labor by learning a few breathing and relaxation techniques. Yes, knowing comfort measures is important, but trying to make your body do what your heart is not able to do will only leave you frustrated and feeling defeated. The stress of labor will bring out your heart because you will not have the energy to hide any attitudes or issues you normally hide. In other words, you will be more yourself in labor than you ever are. So who are you at heart level?

To have true peace during labor you will need the confidence that comes from a heart that loves, trusts and serves Jesus Christ. Remember the Pharisees spent all their time making sure their outsides looked good, but didn't make sure the inside was good. Which do you spend most of your time preparing?

Prayer Guide: Week 20

PRAYING FOR HEALTH

Mom: *Baby:*
Braxton-Hicks contractions   Taste and touch
Anemia   Processing of urine

PRAYING THE BIBLE

Blessed are the pure in heart, for they will see God. *Matthew 5:8*

The goal of this command is love, which comes from a pure heart and a good conscience and a sincere faith. Some have wandered away from these and turned to meaningless talk. *1 Timothy 1:5-6*

SAMPLE PRAYER

Lord,

Look into my heart God and let me see if there is anything in there that needs to be cleaned out. Please refine me, give me a pure heart devoted to you alone. Don't allow me to be distracted by other pursuits; I want to be yours alone.

Send your Spirit to convict me when I hide sin in my heart. Don't allow me to give my heart to anyone but you. Please give me the peace that comes from a right relationship with you.

Amen

Week Twenty One
Pregnancy Week 23

You may find yourself looking quite round in the belly, even though your baby is just now weighing in about a pound. As your baby grows, the placenta grows to keep up with his needs for oxygen and nutrients. The amount of amniotic fluid also increases to ensure he is adequately surrounded and supported.

Your baby's skin is growing at a faster rate than his fat is being deposited which gives him very wrinkly skin. Over the next few months fat will continue to be deposited and will fill in the skin. His skin is also being pigmented, so he will not look see-through anymore. His finger nails are almost fully formed.

The bones in your baby's middle ear are hardening, which is necessary for proper hearing and balance. Over the next few weeks you may find him responding more frequently to the sounds and noises around you.

At this point, your baby is about 8 inches long from crown to rump (20 cm) and weighs around 1 pound (455g). You may be able to get your baby to move by rubbing your abdomen firmly or pressing on one side of your uterus. This early playing with your baby is a normal part of the bonding process, which begins during pregnancy and continues through the first few months of life.

For a Purpose

Reading through the section talking about the priestly garments in Exodus 39, I noticed every piece of clothing had a specific purpose. Somehow everything the priest wore was to remind him what he was doing, who he was doing it for and why he was doing it.

What an amazing idea. Using the very clothing you are wearing to remind you of the importance of what you are doing, using it to keep you alert. It made me think of the powerful reminder the gold chain with charms representing my children is for me. Every time I see or touch it, I think of them and am reminded of my role as their mother.

The same tool could be used during pregnancy and labor. Perhaps a special bracelet, ring or necklace that reminds you of your child. You could use it as a reminder to pray for your child or as an accountability tool when you are struggling with making decisions that will affect your baby's health. You could also use this item during labor, as a focus point and to help keep your mind on the baby.

Prayer Guide: Week 21

PRAYING FOR HEALTH

Mom:
Bonding with baby
Roundness of belly

Baby:
Pigmenting of skin
Fat deposits
Hearing

PRAYING THE BIBLE

I thank my God every time I remember you. In all my prayers for all of you, I always pray with joy. *Philippians 1:3*

I thank God, whom I serve, as my forefathers did, with a clear conscience, as night and day I constantly remember you in my prayers. *1 Timothy 1:3*

SAMPLE PRAYER

Lord,

It is so easy for me to forget what I have learned and to lose my focus. Thank you for giving me tools that remind me to think of my baby and how much you love him. Please help me find the perfect object to remind me to pray for my baby and my whole family. Help me find a way to remind myself to pray for my family as I should. Please teach me to keep the right focus.

Amen

Week Twenty Two
Pregnancy Week 24

This week your little one weighs in at about 1.2 lbs (540 g) and is about 8.5 inches (21 cm) from crown to rump. The total body length (including legs and feet) is somewhere near 12 inches (30 cm) now. She continues to get larger both in length and by muscle growth and fat deposits.

Two big events occur around this time. The first is her lungs are beginning to produce a substance called surfactant. Surfactant is necessary for the lungs to function properly because it prevents the walls of the lungs from sticking to each other when she exhales. The development of the lungs is a long process and will not be complete until she is almost ready to be born.

The other big news is her inner ear may be developed enough to give her a sense of her position in the uterus. The inner ear contains the vestibular system, a collection of fluid filled tubes the body uses to maintain balance. Development of the vestibular system may be part of the reason babies turn head down near the end of pregnancy. Your caregiver will not begin assessing your baby's position for at least another month.

You may be asked to take a Glucose Tolerance Test at your next pre-natal appointment. This test, which assesses your body's ability to metabolize sugar, is recommended because the high estrogen levels of pregnancy can alter your body's production of insulin.

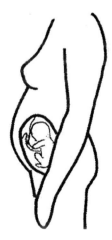

True Rest

This is what the Sovereign Lord,
the Holy One of Israel, says:
"In repentance and rest is your salvation,
in quietness and trust is your strength,
but you would have none of it.
Isaiah 30:15

It seems like it should be so easy to lean on God if rest and quietness are strength and salvation. Who wouldn't love to sit quietly and rest? Unfortunately what we consider rest may not be what God had in mind. It is easy to fool ourselves into thinking we are resting in the Lord, when in reality we are supporting ourselves. It is a little more difficult to fool yourself about repentance and trust. You cannot fake repentance, you cannot fake trust.

If you struggle in any of these areas it is vital that you begin asking God to help you grow. You will need his strength in labor. You see, trust and quietness do not fear labor; they allow labor to progress as it needs to without fighting your body. Rest and repentance don't try to hurry the process of labor and don't assume your plan is better than God's. Instead they allow you to draw on his strength as your body works.

These qualities are your source of strength now, and will continue to be your strength after your baby is born. If you are struggling for strength, stop trying to fight God for control. Submit yourself to him and allow his strength to carry you.

Prayer Guide: Week 22

PRAYING FOR HEALTH

Mom: *Baby:*
Glucose tolerance test   Lung development
                                    Sense of balance

PRAYING THE BIBLE

The Lord protects the simple hearted;
when I was in great need, he saved me.
Be at rest once more, O my soul,
for the Lord has been good to you.
For you, O Lord, have delivered my soul from death,
my eyes from tears,
my feet from stumbling, Psalm *116:6-8*

I have set the Lord always before me.
Because he is at my right hand,
I will not be shaken.
Therefore my heart is glad and my tongue rejoices;
my body also will rest secure,
because you will not abandon me to the grave,
nor will you let your Holy One see decay. *Psalm 16:8-10*

SAMPLE PRAYER

Lord,

I want to rest in your strength. Please help me learn how to rest in you. Show me what it means to be in quietness and to trust you. Teach me how to find your salvation in repentance and rest.

Amen

Week Twenty Three
Pregnancy Week 25

This week your little one weighs in at about 1.2 pounds (540 g) and is about 8.8 inches (22 cm) from crown to rump. At this size, your baby may be big enough to compress your digestive organs. You may find you are not able to eat as much at meals, or you feel heartburn after eating. Many mothers choose to eat smaller meals more frequently, and to remain in an upright position for an hour or two after eating.

Your baby is continuing the process of preparing for life outside the womb. His nostrils are beginning to open, which will allow him to use his nose for breathing. A related development at this time is the blood vessels of the lungs. The lungs will continue to mature almost until your baby is born.

About this time, your baby's spine will begin to form. The spine helps to protect the spinal cord and helps to support your baby in upright positions. The bones and muscles of his hand are developed enough now that he can clench his fingers into a fist.

You may also begin to notice he has rest and alert periods. Many mothers find their baby is most active when they are sitting or resting. Some experts theorize the rocking motion of your body helps to put the baby to sleep, so he is not as active when you are walking or moving.

Joy at the End

> I tell you the truth, you will weep and mourn while
> the world rejoices. You will grieve, but your grief
> will turn to joy. A woman giving birth to a child
> has pain because her time has come; but when
> her baby is born she forgets the anguish because
> of her joy that a child is born into the world. So
> with you: Now is your time of grief, but I will see
> you again and you will rejoice, and no one will
> take away your joy. *John 16:20-22*

It is amazing how much differently we view an event or a struggle we have gone through after it is over. For example, in John 16 Jesus is explaining to his disciples that although they will be filled with sadness for a time, when he returns they will be overfilled with joy. He meant this as an encouragement to his disciples so they would not become discouraged and disheartened while they waited to see him again.

How exciting God used the metaphor of a woman in labor to explain the importance of holding onto the hope and expecting what has been promised. It is important for us to understand that for a time in labor we may feel discouraged and overwhelmed. However in the midst of discouragement we need to look forward to the joy that is coming, the child being born. We must stay focused on the truth that we will see Jesus, he will return no matter how alone or struggling we feel.

Keeping your mind focused during a stressful time takes practice and energy. What a gift God has given us to be able to strengthen our faith and hope in the return of Jesus through our staying focused on the baby during labor. Two promises you can count on: Jesus will return and your labor will end.

Prayer Guide: Week 23

PRAYING FOR HEALTH

Mom: *Baby:*
Difficulty digesting   Nostrils
See baby behavior patterns   Blood supply to lungs
                                Development of spine

PRAYING THE BIBLE

We will shout for joy when you are victorious
and will lift up our banners in the name of our God.
May the Lord grant all your requests.   *Psalm 20:5*

When anxiety was great within me,
your consolation brought joy to my soul.   *Psalm 94:19*

SAMPLE PRAYER

Lord,

I know labor will take more attention, focus and work than I understand. I know in the end, when my baby is born, I will be filled with tremendous joy. Help me to remember and stay focused on the coming joy while I labor.

Even now while I am pregnant and overcome by the normal struggles and trials of life, help me to remember this is all for a purpose. Help me to stay focused on the joy to come.

Amen

Week Twenty Four
Pregnancy Week 26

You should be feeling your baby move regularly now. At just under 2 pounds (910 g) and with about 13 inches (33 cm) of total body length, you may begin to feel the baby move by placing your hand on your swelling belly. She is still very skinny, and her skin looks wrinkly. Over the next few weeks she will bulk up to fill out her skin.

You may begin feeling a painless tightening of the uterus called Braxton-Hicks contractions. Some women recognize them easily; others only know they are having Braxton-Hicks if they happen to touch their abdomen while it is tight.

This week her eyes will begin the process of reopening and she will be able to see. Her brain wave patterns for vision and hearing are similar to a newborn at this point.

She is still working on developing a mature lung system. About this time she is building air sacs in the lungs and producing surfactant, a substance that is necessary for the lungs to fill and empty freely.

Like a Woman in Labor

When the kings joined forces,
when they advanced together,
they saw her and were astounded;
they fled in terror.
Trembling seized them there,
pain like that of a woman in labor.
Psalm 48: 4-6

What is the pain like that of a woman in labor that these warriors felt? What was the trembling that seized them?

The attacking kings tried to advance on Jerusalem, but God made himself the fortress. The warriors were overcome by the sight of God. One look was all it took for them to know he was too powerful for them to defeat. Seeing his power made them aware of their weakness and they fled from him.

In labor you will not have the option to flee the power of God. You will face the strength and power of bringing forth a new life. Seeing this power is overwhelming, and feeling it can be painful. But unlike the warriors who intended to attack God, you will be working with him.

The more you try to fight the power of God in your labor, the more fearful and painful your labor will be. The enemies of God, those who were planning to attack, were overcome by his glory. The Israelites were protected by that same glory. Remember you do not need to be afraid to approach God, you are his daughter and he loves you dearly.

When your labor is completed, you will look back and be astounded just like the kings. You will begin to understand the task was too big and you could never have completed it yourself. You may even be amazed at how much of God's glory you were able to see.

Prayer Guide: Week 24

PRAYING FOR HEALTH ....

Mom: *Baby:*
Feelings of movement   Vision
Braxton-Hicks contractions   Lung development

PRAYING THE BIBLE ....

Who among the gods is like you, O Lord?
Who is like you—
majestic in holiness,
awesome in glory,
working wonders? *Exodus 15:11*

Proclaim the power of God,
whose majesty is over Israel,
whose power is in the skies. *Psalm 68:34*

SAMPLE PRAYER ....

Lord,

I know you are powerful. I know you reign in glory and majesty.
I know my strength looks like weakness compared to you. I
don't want to fight you God.

I want to work with you through this pregnancy and when I give
birth. I want to rely on your strength. I want to be protected by
your glory. I want to look back at my labor and be amazed at
the things you did.

Amen

Week Twenty Five
Pregnancy Week 27

As you begin the third trimester, your baby is tipping the scale around 2 pounds (1000g) and is near 15.5 inches (34 cm) of total length. As your abdomen fills, you may find it difficult to breathe or experience a shortness of breath. This is because of the pressure of the growing uterus on the diaphragm, preventing you from getting a deep breath.

Your baby is at a point of rapid brain growth, and he still needs to mature several systems. The lungs and liver are continuing their development, and the immune system is improving.

The eyelids are opening now, and the retinas (the part of the eye that is sensitive to light) are beginning to form their normal layers. At this point your baby's eyes are either blue/gray or brown/black. However it is normal for eye color to change a few months after birth.

The sounds your baby is hearing are muffled, but he is beginning to recognize certain types of sound. He may begin to recognize voices, especially yours, and over the next few weeks may respond when he hears them.

Recognizing Idols

Every once in a while I like to look over my life and check for idols. They seem to pop up here and there when I least expect them. When I was pregnant with my daughter I struggled with the idol of knowledge. I wanted to know everything, and felt safer when I knew more than the people around me. I allowed myself to even get a bit prideful about how much I knew.

God allowed me to keep that idol and suffer through the consequences of serving it. I expected my knowledge would get me through everything in labor and I was shocked that to actually labor well I needed more than just the knowledge of what to do.

With my son it was different. I had read so many books that gaining more knowledge wasn't of interest to me. Instead I made my ideal birth experience my idol. It wasn't that I was planning anything terrible; it was my attitude about planning. I wasn't open to allowing God to tell me anything other than what I wanted to have happen. For a while, having the perfect birth experience seemed more important to me than anything else.

Like any other idol, God had to snatch that out of my hands. I'm glad he made me give it up before labor began, because I was able to accept my labor as it happened making the best decisions for my baby instead of the best decisions for my perfect labor. In the end God's plan really was better than mine. He gave me everything I asked for and more.

Take some time to look at your own heart this week. Do you have an idol you have been serving during this pregnancy?

Prayer Guide: Week 25

PRAYING FOR HEALTH

Mom:
Shortness of breath

Baby:
Immune system
Rapid brain growth
Recognizing voices

PRAYING THE BIBLE

"You shall have no other gods before me. *Exodus 20:3*

Exalt the Lord our God and worship at his footstool;
he is holy. *Psalm 99:5*

SAMPLE PRAYER

Lord,

It is so easy to get wrapped up into the belief that something other than you will save me or help me or protect me. It is so easy to seek knowledge or experiences or praise instead of seeking you alone. I know I am easily swayed by idols.

Please give me wisdom as I go through this pregnancy. Don't allow me to fool myself, and don't allow others to fool me. When I begin to serve, seek or worship something or someone other than you make it clear to me and correct me right away. I don't want anything to get in the way of my love for you.

Amen

Week Twenty Six
Pregnancy Week 28

At 2.4 pounds (1100g) and 15.75 inches (35 cm) your baby is still looking rather thin. Only about 2-3% of her weight is body fat right now, but that will change soon. From crown to rump she is about 10 inches (25 cm).

The rapid brain growth that started last week is continuing. Not only is the amount of brain tissue increasing, but the brain design is becoming more mature. It is forming the grooves and indentations characteristic of a human brain.

Along with the developing brain come developing senses. This week your baby's eyes are completely formed and opened. She can see, but the view is dark and blurry inside the bag of waters. It is believed that the difference between the brightness of day and the darkness of night can be seen in the uterus, however bright light would come through as a dull reddish glow.

Your baby may be able to recognize your voice by now. You may find her responding by moving or suddenly being still when she hears loud noises. It is ok to read, sing and talk to your baby. This helps encourage good bonding.

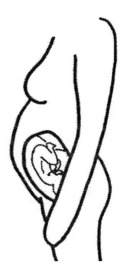

Fire and Water

When you pass through the waters,
I will be with you;
and when you pass through the rivers,
they will not sweep over you.
When you walk through the fire,
you will not be burned;
the flames will not set you ablaze.
Isaiah 43:2

It may be irreverent, but I can't help but think of birth when I read these verses.

Inside the uterus, your baby is living in a water-filled sac. When it comes time for your baby to be born, this sac will break and some of the water will exit your body. Some of the water will be trapped behind your baby and will not be emptied until your baby's head has been pushed out of your body.

The vaginal opening stretches to allow your baby to exit your body without causing damage to you. As the skin stretches, the tightening and pulling cause a burning sensation which signals your body to stop pushing to allow the skin to stretch. This burning sensation is commonly referred to as the Ring of Fire.

So every time I read these verses I remember it as God's promise to me and my baby that passing through the water and fire of labor will not overcome us, we will not be harmed. It is my promise from God that he will be with me.

Prayer Guide: Week 26

PRAYING FOR HEALTH

Mom: *Baby:*
Shortness of breath   Sight
                                Rapid brain growth

PRAYING THE BIBLE

Yet I am always with you;
you hold me by my right hand.
You guide me with your counsel,
and afterward you will take me into glory. *Psalm 73:23-24*

So do not fear, for I am with you;
do not be dismayed, for I am your God.
I will strengthen you and help you;
I will uphold you with my righteous right hand. *Isaiah 41:10*

SAMPLE PRAYER

Lord,

I am so glad you are with me and my baby and you will not leave us during this pregnancy or during my baby's birth. You are faithful to your promises, and you will not leave us.

Help me to remember you will be there. Help me to call on you when I feel alone or frightened. Give me the eyes to see you when I need you the most. Thank you for your faithfulness.

Amen

Week Twenty Seven
Pregnancy Week 29

This week, at about 2.7 pounds (125g) and 16.7 inches (37 cm) of total length, your baby's head is finally getting into proportion with the rest of his body. Your abdomen may be feeling full, and you may find yourself feeling uncomfortable.

Your baby will continue to accumulate fat this week which will help to plump him up. If you could look at him, you would notice that his eyes can now move in the sockets – he can look around without turning his head.

One major change this week is that your baby's brain has matured enough to begin controlling breathing and body temperature regulation. Remember body functions rely on more than just brain control. The lungs need to continue their maturation process for your child to breathe properly. His body needs to put on more fat to help with temperature regulation, but even when he is born his ability to maintain body temperature will be minimal.

Another change this week occurs in your baby's endocrine system. The adrenal glands (near the kidneys) begin to produce androgen and estrogen. The presence of these hormones in the blood stream stimulates the production of prolactin in your system. Prolactin is the hormone that stimulates your breasts to produce colostrum. Some women will leak fluid from the breasts, however this is not necessary to breastfeed successfully.

Mothering

It is normal to feel some bit of nervousness when you are being faced with a new challenge, and mothering is no exception. Many women find themselves concerned with how they will handle the stress and demands of mothering. How are they going to feed the baby, change the diapers, get the baby to sleep and all the other things that must be done. In many ways, we let how efficient we are at completing these tasks be the gage of our success at mothering.

Its not that these physical needs are unimportant, they are important to your baby's health. However these things are eternally insignificant. There is no test in heaven for how easily you can get a baby to fall asleep, how long your baby can go without eating or how quickly you are able to change a diaper.

Instead, as you think about the challenges awaiting you as a new mother focus your energy on the eternally significant mothering skills. How effective are you at modeling love and serving God? How good is your ability to love unselfishly? What example do you give your child for forgiving and seeking forgiveness? These are the important skills of mothering. These are the skills that are going to make a difference in your child's life.

Prayer Guide: Week 27

PRAYING FOR HEALTH

Mom:
Feeling full or uncomfortable
Breasts leaking fluid

Baby:
Fat deposits
Movement of eyes
Brain control of body
Adrenal glands

PRAYING THE BIBLE

Fathers, do not exasperate your children; instead, bring them up in the training and instruction of the Lord. *Ephesians 6:4*

Come, my children, listen to me;
I will teach you the fear of the Lord. *Psalm 34:11*

SAMPLE PRAYER

Lord,

Thank you for the opportunity to care for one of your children. Help me to remember I am not only caring for a physical body that will decay. Remind me this child has an eternal soul in need of as much feeding and care as his physical form.

Help me to be wise in my decision making. Help me to keep my priorities in the proper order. Help me to mother my child's soul as much as I mother his body.

Amen

Week Twenty Eight
Pregnancy Week 30

This week your baby is about 3 pounds (1360 grams) and is about 17 inches (38 cm) total length. From head to rump she is about 11 inches (28 cm). Over the next few weeks she will continue to gain weight as her body prepares for life outside the womb.

As always, your baby is growing and maturing all the body systems. The focus now seems to be on the lungs. She is moving her diaphragm to mimic breathing movements. While this does help her to prepare to breathe when she is born, it can cause some hiccups. Most mothers can feel the rhythmic pulses caused by hiccups in an unborn child.

While she practices working her muscles, her lungs continue to build a supply of surfactant. There is a protein in the surfactant that some experts believe triggers hormonal changes in the mother and baby. These hormonal changes are the beginning stages of your body preparing to give birth. We can marvel at how perfectly God designed this system of growing babies, that when the final touches near completion, the baby begins the birth process.

Another important point this week is your baby's bone marrow has matured enough to be producing her red blood cells. Every day she becomes more able to handle life in the world. If you have not already, you will soon be getting Braxton-Hicks contractions. Think of them as little reminders that God did not intend for your child to stay in your belly forever.

The Feast of Trumpets
Leviticus 23

The number seven is a representation of completion, and in the Jewish calendar this importance is heightened by the celebration of three feasts during the seventh month to end the religious year. The Feast of Trumpets, the first of these feasts which are known as the "High Holy Days," marks this completion with the blowing of trumpets. This was to serve as a reminder to the Israelites of the upcoming atonement and a call to repentance.

In the gestation timeline, the Feast of Trumpets occurs when the mother is aware of the baby's ability to respond to sounds. This means the baby is able to hear, and is large enough to move or kick in such a way that the mother understands the movement occurred because of the sound. Just as the Feast of Trumpets signals the beginning of the end for the Jewish religious calendar, your baby's ability to respond to sounds signals the beginning of the end of the pregnancy.

What an amazing way God has chosen to demonstrate how developed your baby is already! The fact that your baby changes activity when stimulated is an indicator to you that she is already beginning to learn how to interact with her environment. As you talk and sing to her, you may find that she develops routines for responding to you. In some ways, the responsiveness of your baby is a signal of the end of your pregnancy, a reminder to prepare yourself for the upcoming labor and infancy stages.

The Israelites celebrate the Feast of Trumpets by observing a day of rest. Although this was a nation wide feast, it was an intensely personal celebration in which the individual came before God to seek forgiveness. Use the special reminder of your baby's interactions with you as a call to prepare for labor, when you will stand before God relying on his strength and grace.

Please see the acknowledgement page in the front of the book for more information about Zola Levitt Ministries, Inc.

Prayer Guide: Week 28

PRAYING FOR HEALTH ⸺⸺⸺⸺⸺⸺⸺⸺⸺⸺⸺⸺

Mom: *Baby:*
Braxton-Hicks contractions   Lungs
                                   Hiccups
                                   Bone marrow

PRAYING THE BIBLE ⸺⸺⸺⸺⸺⸺⸺⸺⸺⸺⸺⸺⸺

Praise the Lord.
Praise God in his sanctuary;
praise him in his mighty heavens.
Praise him for his acts of power;
praise him for his surpassing greatness.
Praise him with the sounding of the trumpet,
praise him with the harp and lyre,
praise him with tambourine and dancing,
praise him with the strings and flute,
praise him with the clash of cymbals,
praise him with resounding cymbals.
Let everything that has breath praise the Lord.
Praise the Lord. *Psalm 150*

SAMPLE PRAYER ⸺⸺⸺⸺⸺⸺⸺⸺⸺⸺⸺⸺⸺

Lord,

Thank you for the reminder of my baby's responses. I know he is almost ready to be born, and I know this is a call to attention on my part. Let every interaction with my baby be a reminder to me to praise you for the miracle you are working inside me.

Amen

Week Twenty Nine
Pregnancy Week 31

The fat your baby has been growing has increased his size to 3.5 lbs (1600 g) and has given his skin a pink appearance. He's continuing to grow, and his bones are hardening. This week he is about 18 inches (40 cm) in total length. Over the next two weeks he will mature enough that his chances of survival if born early will be pretty good. About 30% of triplets and 10% of twins are born at this time, however most often it is best for babies to stay in the uterus as long as possible.

Your baby is beginning a time of very rapid brain development. Although you may be uncomfortable eating due to heartburn or indigestion, continue your good nutrition so your baby will have the best brain possible. He can already respond to light by having his irises contract and dilate.

His little body is urinating about half a liter of fluid a day. The fluid is emptied into the bag of waters, which is completely cleaned and new every three hours. Your caregiver may start to monitor the amount of fluids in your bag of waters at this point. Too much or too little fluid is a sign to your midwife to check for possible problems. Because the fluid refreshes itself on a three hour cycle, it is important to keep yourself well hydrated.

The pressure of the baby may begin to cause aches in your pelvis and your back. Be sure to use good posture and perform exercises to help strengthen the muscles of your back. Many women find they get the best sleep when they use a variety of pillows to help support the weight.

The Day of Atonement
Leviticus 23

The Day of Atonement is a day of freedom. Once a year each individual was to stand before God to receive forgiveness for his sins, to be cleansed. Last week, the Feast of Trumpets was a call to repentance, this week the Day of Atonement is the cleansing.

As gestation mirrors the scheduling of the feasts, the Day of Atonement occurs when the baby's body begins increasing its amounts of hemoglobin A (adult hemoglobin) and decreasing hemoglobin F (fetal hemoglobin). Fetal hemoglobin is uniquely designed to transport oxygen through the body of a developing baby. Hemoglobin A is better suited to life outside the womb and will remain the dominate hemoglobin throughout adult life.

It is important to note that hemoglobin F is not changed into hemoglobin A. They are two different substances produced by the body. As your baby grows, the hemoglobin F production will decrease and hemoglobin A will increase. In effect, your baby's blood will be new.

Just like the Day of Atonement in the religious calendar, the Day of Atonement in the gestational calendar is a day of freedom. The change in blood makes your baby a new creation, able to live outside of the womb. This is remarkably similar to the way repentance and forgiveness make a Christian a new creation, able to live in heaven.

Please see the acknowledgement page in the front of the book for more information about Zola Levitt Ministries, Inc.

Prayer Guide: Week 29

PRAYING FOR HEALTH

Mom: *Baby:*
Bag of Waters   Rapid brain growth
Pressure on back or pelvis   Weight gain
Posture

PRAYING THE BIBLE

Therefore, if anyone is in Christ, he is a new creation; the old has gone, the new has come! *2 Corinthians 5:17*

It is for freedom that Christ has set us free. Stand firm, then, and do not let yourselves be burdened again by a yoke of slavery. *Galatians 5:1*

SAMPLE PRAYER

Lord,

I know the power of Christ's blood makes me new and able to live with God. Thank you for writing a reminder of this into my pregnancy. I praise you because of your amazing power and wisdom.

You have created my baby perfectly to live inside me until he is ready, and then to live out in the world. I am amazed by the glory of your design not just for physical life, but for spiritual life as well. You created me perfectly to be adopted into your kingdom. Thank you.

Amen

Week Thirty
Pregnancy Week 32

The weight continues to pile on, with your baby weighing in around 4 pounds (1800 g) this week. She continues to strengthen and lengthen her muscles, with the average body length around 18 ½ inches (42 cm). As you move closer to the time of birth, you may begin seeing your caregiver every two weeks.

Your little bundle of joy is looking more and more like the baby you imagine in your mind every day. Her finger and toenails have formed and are growing. She also has eyelashes and eyebrows. Hair is even growing on the top of her head. The lanugo hair that protected her body from the amniotic fluid is beginning to fall off.

In addition to looking like a newborn, your baby is beginning to react like a newborn. All five of her senses are now functioning. Your baby can see differences of light and dark through your skin, can hear what happens around you and within you, tastes the amniotic fluid, and feels the closeness of your uterine wall. This is also a peak week of movement for your baby. Soon, her size will restrict her to shifting instead of all-out kicks.

Some women find as they near the birth day, their breasts begin to leak colostrum. This is normal. However it is not necessary to leak colostrum to be successful at breastfeeding. Whether or not you leak is simply a matter of hormonal levels.

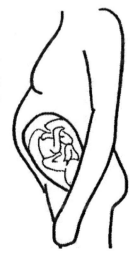

The Feast of Tabernacles
Leviticus 23

The final feast of Israel is the Feast of Tabernacles. This is a joyful feast that happens after the fields have been harvested, and after all Israel has been forgiven of its sins. Members of the community live in tabernacles or huts in remembrance of the 40 years spent wandering the desert. Part of the joy is remembering the glory of the presence of God dwelling among the Israelites in the Tabernacle.

The Feast of Tabernacles falls in between agricultural cycles. The people are thankful for what God has blessed them with so far and look expectantly to the coming rains which will provide for the next crops. So in one part we have the significance of the completion of one cycle of growth for the baby and the expectation of the next cycle of growth (outside the womb).

Zola Levitt found that symbolism also lies in the baby's lungs, which are mature enough that the baby would probably survive if born at this time. The presence of the "breath of life" is reflected in the feast because the Tabernacle was built to house the Spirit of God as the Israelites traveled through the desert. Also, in Ezekiel 37:8-10, God tells Ezekiel to prophesy to the four winds to breathe on the dead bones that they may become alive. The meaning of the feast of tabernacles to gestation then is the presence of breathing.

The Feast of Tabernacles is the only one of the feasts that does not have a New Testament fulfillment, and so its remembrance to Christians is not just a historical remembrance of the events of the desert wanderings, but also a future remembrance to the upcoming harvest of souls when Christ comes again. Let this feast remind you also that your baby is not merely flesh and blood, but also is an eternal soul who Christ is longing to gather home at the end of this age.

Please see the acknowledgement page in the front of the book for more information about Zola Levitt Ministries, Inc.

Prayer Guide: Week 30

PRAYING FOR HEALTH

Mom:	*Baby:*
Frequent health care visits	Finger and toe nails
Change in baby movements	Eye brows and lashes
Leaking breasts	All five senses

PRAYING THE BIBLE

The Spirit of God has made me;
the breath of the Almighty gives me life. *Job 33:4*

When you send your Spirit,
they are created,
and you renew the face of the earth. *Psalm 104:30*

SAMPLE PRAYER

Lord,

The breath of your spirit is life to me. Thank you for breathing life into my baby. Don't let me forget that my child is not only a child of flesh and blood, but a spiritual being as well. Help me to look at him with your eyes, to see the eternal soul his body holds.

As my child and I move to the next season of growth, I am humbled to see the wisdom of your timing and plan. You have designed every cell of my baby. He is made according to your design. Help me to be as careful with the next season of his growth as I have been with this one.

Amen

Week Thirty One
Pregnancy Week 33

This week your baby will once again pick up the speed with which he gains weight. Weighing in at about 4.4 pounds (2000g) and measuring about 19.4 inches (43 cm), you are probably wondering how your belly can expand to fit any more growth. That is part of the wonder of God's creation, your abdomen can expand and you will survive.

Your baby's brain is functioning well and receiving messages from his senses. Even before he is born he is able to learn about his surroundings. It is important to realize your baby is a complete human being, which includes not only physical needs but also emotional needs. Some experts believe for the first few weeks of life, babies feel most comfortable in environments that mimic the womb because it feels "safe" amid all the changes they are experiencing.

Another exciting change in your baby's brain is he now experiences REM (Rapid Eye Movement) sleep. This is the deep stage of sleep where dreaming occurs. He sleeps a lot too. You have probably begun to be familiar with his daily patterns of awake and sleep just by paying attention to his movements.

His lungs are nearly mature. The surfactant that coats them is continuing to be laid down, and his practice breathing continues to cause hiccups. In addition to the frequent hiccups, you may find yourself experiencing frequent contractions. These practice contractions are beneficial because they help strengthen the uterine muscle.

Working with God

Adam lay with his wife Eve, and she became
pregnant and gave birth to Cain. She said, "With
the help of the Lord I have brought forth a man."
Genesis 4:1

When Eve gave birth to Cain, the first baby ever born, she did
not take credit for it herself.   Instead, she recognized he was
born because God helped and she worked.

Sometimes it is easy to fall into the trap of thinking it is all
me. This line of thinking tells me what I do is vital so if I mess
up it will be a major disaster. This kind of thinking acts as if God
put us on the earth and left, and because he is no longer
involved, we humans have to do it all. What terrible pressure
that would put on us!

Sometimes it is easy to fall into the trap of thinking it is all
God. This line of thinking tells me God is always in control, so it
doesn't matter what I do. Because the will of God always
happens,   I can relax and just let it happen. How meaningless
that would make our lives.

Eve knew life happened in a relationship with God, as he
works his plan. We play our part through obeying his word. As
you prepare for labor and parenting remember God has a plan,
but you must follow. This is a team effort. Don't go without him,
and don't send him without you.

Prayer Guide: Week 31

PRAYING FOR HEALTH

Mom:
Stretching of abdomen
Braxton-Hicks contractions

Baby:
Increased weight gain
Learning about surroundings
REM sleep

PRAYING THE BIBLE

With God we will gain the victory,
and he will trample down our enemies. *Psalm 60:12*

For I know that through your prayers and the help given by the
Spirit of Jesus Christ, what has happened to me will turn out for
my deliverance. *Philippians 1:19*

SAMPLE PRAYER

Lord,

You are my helper, and I am willing to be used for your purpose.
Don't allow me to think too highly of myself, putting the full
weight of the world on my shoulders. But also, don't allow me to
put the full responsibility for the world on you as if my serving
you has no impact.

Help me to be wise in the decisions I make. Give me the eyes to
see what you have laid before me to do, and give me the
strength and courage to do it.

Amen

Week Thirty Two
Pregnancy Week 34

The increased size of your baby may begin to make her too big for your abdominal cavity. Not to worry, your baby will "drop" her head into your pelvis to give her body a little more room. When this happens you may find you breathe and eat a little easier. Just for the record, she is about 5 pounds (2275 g) and 19.8 inches (44 cm) this week.

The drop into the pelvis may help relieve some of the stomach pressure, but it can increase the pelvic pressure you feel. Be sure you are doing pelvic floor exercises every day. Additionally, doing exercises to strengthen your lower back can help prevent some back ache. As always, focus on using good posture and good body mechanics to help prevent discomfort.

Her body is very mature, and her lungs are well-developed which gives her good chances of survival if she were born this week. The vernix (white substance protecting her skin) is thicker, while the lanugo hair is almost completely gone. Her finger nails have grown to the end of her fingers, and she urinates almost a pint of fluid a day.

You may begin to feel tingling or sensitivity in your breasts again this week. Your baby's adrenal glands and the placenta are both producing hormones which stimulate your body to begin milk production.

Consecrate Yourself

Joshua told the people, "Consecrate yourselves, for tomorrow the Lord will do amazing things among you." *Joshua 3:5*

When Joshua told the Israelites to consecrate themselves, he was directing them to wash with soap and water and to abstain from sexual relations. This consecration cleaned the body and prepared it to meet with God. On one level it was a reflection of the holiness of God, and on another level it gave the Israelites the time needed to reflect on the greatness of God and prepare to be with him.

I love the idea of consecration as a time of preparation for giving birth, although I'm not really a stickler for the process of it. Giving myself a few hours to relax in a warm bath, listen to some praise and worship music, pour out my heart to God and listen to his replies helps keep me in a right relationship with him. I learn so much from the times I spend with God when I plan to give him an hour or more at a time.

How can you consecrate your heart to prepare for the amazing things God is about to do in your life? Your time of consecration could be as simple as a cup of tea in your living room with some music and your Bible; or as elaborate as checking into a hotel for an evening to spend time focusing just on him. Perhaps you need to sit by a lake or go for a walk in the woods to prepare your heart to meet God in labor. The idea is simply to plan at least an hour to be alone with God doing whatever connects you to him. Whatever you choose, remember this is a time of preparation so you will be ready to meet God and see the amazing things he does while you labor.

Prayer Guide: Week 32

PRAYING FOR HEALTH

Mom: *Baby:*
Baby "dropping"   Vernix and lanugo hair
Pelvic floor exercises   Adrenal hormone production
Good posture

PRAYING THE BIBLE

A voice of one calling:
"In the desert prepare
the way for the Lord;
make straight in the wilderness
a highway for our God." *Isaiah 40:3*

Consecrate yourselves and be holy,
because I am the Lord your God. *Leviticus 20:7*

SAMPLE PRAYER

Lord,

Help me find a way to prepare myself so I am ready to meet with you and work with you during labor. Give me the eyes to see opportunities surrounding me and give me the ability and strength to take advantage of those opportunities.

Let me be prepared for labor. As I work to prepare my home and my body, please prepare my heart. Give me a right focus and the wisdom to make decisions.

Amen

Week Thirty Three
Pregnancy Week 35

At this point, the average weight gain for moms is 24 – 29 pounds. Notice this says average, not normal. You may have gained more or less, and as long as you are eating healthy and exercising you can be sure your body is gaining the weight it needs. If you are concerned you have not eaten healthy or exercised your body it is never too late to start.

You are probably getting anxious for labor to begin. You may even be requesting cervical checks to see if you are dilated. Unfortunately, even if you have begun to dilate it is no indicator for when labor will begin. Your best bet is to keep yourself as comfortable, well nourished and rested as possible.

Be sure to stay well hydrated by drinking water to thirst. Caffeinated drinks act as diuretics, meaning they pull water out of your body rather than hydrating you. Proper hydration is important for maintaining adequate amniotic fluid levels because the fluid replenishes itself every three hours.

There is a wide variation in the size of babies by this time. The average is around 5.5 pounds (2550 g) and about 20.25 inches (45 cm) long. You are entering the time of most rapid weight gain, where your baby will be gaining ½ to ¾ of a pound each week. Fat is being deposited all over her body, and the final touches are being made to all the organ systems.

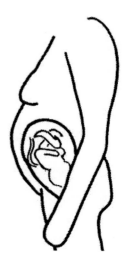

Potential

It is amazing to read the story of the birth of John in Luke chapter 1 and wonder, "Did his mother have any idea who her baby was?" What must it have been like to rock him, knowing his potential? Did she focus extra time and attention to his religious studies because she knew he was going to be used by God?

Of course Elizabeth did have the angel tell her about the importance of John. His conception was a miracle. How could she not raise her child with eager expectation?

Your baby is every bit as important to the work of God as John was. Your baby was created for a purpose determined by God, and you are the perfect parent for your child so he will be able to complete that purpose. God did not make a mistake; you can help your child become the man or woman God intended for him or her to be.

As you prepare to hold your baby, remember she is just as important to God as John was. She has just as big a part to play in his kingdom. God created her for a purpose and God gave her you to help her find that purpose

Prayer Guide: Week 33

PRAYING FOR HEALTH

Mom: *Baby:*
Healthy eating and exercise   Rapid weight gain
Patience until "birth" day   Fat stores

PRAYING THE BIBLE

Many are the plans in a man's heart,
but it is the Lord's purpose that prevails. *Proverbs 19:21*

For I know the plans I have for you," declares the Lord, "plans to prosper you and not to harm you, plans to give you hope and a future. *Jeremiah 29:11*

SAMPLE PRAYER

Lord,

You have created my baby with a purpose. I know you have a plan for him, even though I cannot see that plan yet. Help me to remember this child has a purpose to fulfill for you.

Give me wisdom and strength to lead him into a loving relationship with you. Help me to model obedience to your law and a love for your people. Help me to be the mother you created me to be.

Amen

Week Thirty Four
Pregnancy Week 36

Your uterus is probably up under your ribs and you may be feeling that you have run out of room. This is normal, and to be expected since your baby is now about 20.7 inches (46 cm) long and weighs in around 6 pounds (2750 g). Babies vary in weight from 3 to 6.5 pounds at this point, with the size depending on a number of variables including genetics, the mother's nutrition and overall health.

You will probably start seeing your caregiver once a week until the end of your pregnancy. Use this time to finalize any plans for labor you did not yet discuss with your midwife. Your caregiver will be checking for general indicators of health, as well as the position of the baby. About 7% of babies are in a head down (breech) position at this point. By week 38 of gestation (week 40 of pregnancy), only about 4% will remain breech.

You may have discovered an increased need to urinate. This is caused by the increased pressure on your bladder from your baby's head. Her skull is fully formed, however it remains soft enough to mold to the birth canal. This is partly managed by the skull bones staying separate until after birth. You may be familiar with the "soft spot" on a baby's head; this is because the bones of the skull are not fused. Your baby's skull will not be fully fused and hardened until after her first birthday.

You are nearly done. It is not easy sharing your body with another person, but you have come so far. If you are feeling the desire to give up, be sure to go to God who will give you the strength you need to continue to care for other family members. If needed, be sure to enlist the help of loved ones. It is important to begin getting as much rest as possible.

Illusion of Control

In Luke chapter 8 Jesus and the disciples are in a boat crossing the sea. A storm starts blowing and the disciples are frightened. Jesus is asleep in the boat, and his followers wake him because they fear the boat will sink. Jesus calmly rebuked the storm and all was quiet.

When Jesus calmed the storm the disciples were amazed and fearful because Jesus had the power to calm the wind and the water. However, Jesus only changed the view from the boat; he didn't really change their circumstances. You see, he told them they were going to the other side of the water, and the other side of the water was where he was taking them. It didn't matter to Jesus if the wind was blowing.

The disciples were never in danger, but they felt like they were in danger because they felt out of control. They were focused on what was happening around them instead of who was with them. They lost site of the fact that the control was never theirs to begin with. Calm seas or stormy seas, the disciples never had control. Control was just an illusion that gave them security. In effect, feeling in control was a false faith for them.

Think of this when you begin making preparations for labor. In the midst of a storm or in the calm seas you are not the one in control. You may feel you can control the circumstances and the view around you as you labor, but like the disciples it is just an illusion. Trust God who is in control in the midst of a storm. Remember, the environment is not in control of the Spirit, it is the Spirit who controls the environment.

Prayer Guide: Week 34

PRAYING FOR HEALTH

Mom:	*Baby:*
Feeling "out of room"	Position
Frequent health care visits	Molding of the skull to pelvis
Frequent urination	
Rest	

PRAYING THE BIBLE

There is no wisdom, no insight, no plan
that can succeed against the Lord. *Proverbs 21:30*

Yours, O Lord, is the greatness and the power
and the glory and the majesty and the splendor,
for everything in heaven and earth is yours.
Yours, O Lord, is the kingdom;
you are exalted as head over all. *1 Chronicles 29:11*

SAMPLE PRAYER

Lord,

I know it is you who have the power, and I am not in control.
But sometimes I forget, and sometimes I put my faith in my own
sense of control. Please don't let me be fooled by that illusion as
I prepare for labor.

Help me to remember it is not about what is going on around me
that is important, but it is my heart. Let the Holy Spirit direct the
room, and keep me trusting you even in the midst of a storm.

Amen

Week Thirty Five
Pregnancy Week 37

The end of this week your baby will be considered "full term," which means you have reached the low end of the average time for gestation. Your baby is about 6.5 pounds (2950 g) and 21 inches (47 cm) long. He will continue to put on weight at about a half ounce a day, until birth.

His lungs are completing the maturation process, and he continues to practice his breathing movements. His muscle and brain development is enough that he can grasp things in his fingers and turn his body towards a source of light.

You may notice an increase in the cervical mucus now, as your body chemistry changes to prepare to give birth. Your body will also continue to "practice" for labor with Braxton-Hicks contractions until the real thing starts. All these practice contractions can affect the cervix, making it softer, thinning it out and sometimes beginning the process of dilation. This doesn't mean you will be heading into labor soon, just that you will have less work to do once labor begins.

Some women find the cervical dilation from Braxton-Hicks contractions is enough to release the mucus plug from the cervix. The mucus plug is a protection for the uterus during pregnancy, and as the cervix begins to open, the mucus is unable to be held in place. It is not necessary for it to fall out until labor starts, and you may not even notice when it does.

Benefits from the Work of Others

> When the Lord your God brings you into the land
> he swore to your fathers, to Abraham, Isaac and
> Jacob, to give you—a land with large, flourishing
> cities you did not build, houses filled with all kinds
> of good things you did not provide, wells you did
> not dig, and vineyards and olive groves you did not
> plant—then when you eat and are satisfied, be
> careful that you do not forget the Lord, who
> brought you out of Egypt, out of the land of
> slavery.
> *Deuteronomy 6:10-12*

Have you ever considered how much of your life is lived receiving the blessings of other peoples work? For most of us, we do not live in homes we have built, wear clothes we have sewn or cook food we have grown. God has blessed us greatly through the work of other individuals.

As you prepare for labor, you may hear well-meaning encouragers say, "Women have been having babies for thousands of years so you'll survive." Perhaps a more encouraging way to look at it would be women have been having babies for thousands of years, and you get to reap the benefits of thousands of years of experience.

When you labor, you do not need to "figure it all out" on your own. The births of countless babies through generations have taught us techniques to help labor progress normally and to keep you as comfortable as possible while you labor. Once again, you will be benefiting from the work of other people. Enjoy this blessing from God.

Prayer Guide: Week 35

PRAYING FOR HEALTH

Mom:
Braxton-Hicks contractions
Cervical changes

Baby:
Practice breathing
Muscle coordination

PRAYING THE BIBLE

May God be gracious to us and bless us
and make his face shine upon us,
Selah. Psalm 67:1

Then they can train the younger women to love their husbands
and children. Titus 2:4

SAMPLE PRAYER

Lord,

I can't believe how much you bless me through the work of
others. So much in my life has come from others. Thank you
that I am not alone, and don't need to make everything myself.

Thank you that I can benefit from the experiences of so many
women before me. Please help me to find women who can give
me encouragement in these last few days of pregnancy.

Amen

Week Thirty Six
Pregnancy Week 38

Your baby may be gaining as much as an ounce a day as the fat continues to be deposited; however the overall growth has slowed down. Your baby weighs in around 6.8 pounds (3100 g) and is about 21 inches (47 cm) in length. Your weight gain has probably slowed down, and your pre-labor contractions (Braxton-Hicks) may continue to increase.

The pressure of the baby's head in your pelvis stretches it considerably. As your body is washed with hormones that soften cartilage, the flexibility in your pelvis increases even more. You may feel wobbly as you walk not only because of the stretched pelvis, but because these hormones will loosen every joint in your body.

If your baby is a boy, his testicles have descended into the scrotum now. If your baby is a girl, her labia have developed. Because she has been practicing sucking and swallowing with the amniotic fluid, there is beginning to be a build-up of waste materials in the intestines. This material is called meconium, and will be your baby's first bowel movements.

Expectancy

Though the fig tree does not bud and there are no grapes on the vines, though the olive crop fails and the fields produce no food, though there are no sheep in the pen and no cattle in the stalls, yet I will rejoice in the Lord, I will be joyful in God my Savior. The Sovereign Lord is my strength; he makes my feet like the feet of a deer, he enables me to go on the heights. Habakkuk 3: 17-19

This time of waiting expectantly, knowing God has something good for you but not yet being able to see it can feel like a trial. You do not know what will happen, but you do have some certainties that you can trust in.

Even though there are not contractions yet, and the bag of waters has not broken, even though you cannot hear your baby cry or nurse him at your breast, you can rejoice in the Lord. You can rejoice because the Lord is preparing you for what is coming. You may not need the feet of a deer to scale a mountain, but God is preparing your heart and body to labor and to mother your child.

Spend some time being joyful in God. Put on some praise music and dance around. Walk outside enjoying the fresh air. Write a note to your baby letting him know how excited you are, and how much you can't wait to meet him face to face. Find some way to express your joy this week.

Prayer Guide: Week 36

PRAYING FOR HEALTH

Mom:	*Baby:*
Stretching of pelvis	Weight gain
Hormonal prep for labor	Meconium
Wobbly feeling when walking	

PRAYING THE BIBLE

You have made known to me the path of life;
you will fill me with joy in your presence,
with eternal pleasures at your right hand. *Psalm 16:11*

Praise the Lord with the harp;
make music to him on the ten-stringed lyre.
Sing to him a new song;
play skillfully, and shout for joy.
For the word of the Lord is right and true;
he is faithful in all he does. *Psalm 33:2-4*

SAMPLE PRAYER

Lord,

I know I am not holding my baby yet. I know I can't hear him cry or look into his eyes yet. I am joyful anyway because I know you are with me and with my baby. I know you promise to stay with us no matter what happens.

Thank you for the opportunity to be a mother. Thank you for this child. Thank you that you trust me with one of your children. Thank you for showing me the miracles that go along with a new life. Thank you for the way you have been my strength and will continue to do so.

Amen

Week Thirty Seven
Pregnancy Week 39

At around 7 pounds (3250 g), your baby is still gaining weight. There is not much room left for him to move around. At this stage the umbilical cord is about 20 inches (50 cm) long and about half an inch (1.3 cm) thick. Things are getting pretty crowded inside you, so the movements slow down and your baby is forced deeper into the pelvis. Some babies do not move into the pelvis until labor begins, others have already dropped in place. Dropping does increase the room for your lungs, but it increases the pressure on your bladder. It will also change your center of gravity which can add to the unsteady on your feet feeling some women get.

Your baby is increasing surfactant production for the lungs to prepare for labor. He is also benefiting from your antibodies, which are supplied to him through the placenta. Most of the lanugo hair is gone, and the vernix is disappearing.

As your body prepares to give birth, you may find yourself having more frequent contractions, even going through periods of "pre-labor" where you have regular contractions for an hour or more but then go away. Your cervix is softening to prepare to open, however you may be completely unaware of these changes.

You will know you are in labor when the contractions do not stop or slow down with time. You may also see some blood tinged mucus (bloody show) when you use the bathroom, and have loose stools for several hours. All these are indicators your body is in the very early stages of labor. In true labor the contractions get progressively longer and stronger and happen at closer intervals. Although it sounds silly, you will not wonder if you are in labor when you are really in labor.

Focus

Did you know your eyes, even though they can see everything in front of you only focus on one small piece of the scene? One part comes in clear, the rest gets fuzzy or fades into the background so you just don't notice it. This is why when you get your photos back from the developer they never seem to look as good as you thought. The entire background that your eye naturally ignored could not be ignored by the camera.

In order to change your focus, you either need something to move or change so it gets your attention, or you need the desire to change your focus and then look somewhere else.

This can work to your advantage if your focus is on Christ. But if your focus is not on Christ you will need to force your focus to change.

It can be difficult in these late stages of pregnancy to keep your focus on Christ. With the difficulties sleeping, eating and sometimes even moving is it any wonder you feel exhausted and unmotivated? But you must clear your field of vision and focus your attention on Christ. Labor will be here before you know it, and you won't have the energy during labor to move your attention back to Jesus, so if your focus is wrong, do everything you can to change it now.

Prayer Guide: Week 37

PRAYING FOR HEALTH

Mom: *Baby:*
Uncomfortable fullness   Finding room
Pre-labor   Antibody protection
Cervical changes
Recognizing true labor

PRAYING THE BIBLE

My ears had heard of you but now my eyes have seen you.
Job 42:5

Turn my eyes away from worthless things; preserve my life according to your word. *Psalm 119:37*

SAMPLE PRAYER

Lord,

Don't let my eyes get distracted by the world around me. Even as I prepare for such a great change in my life help me to keep my focus on you first. Let me follow where you lead.

If my focus is on the wrong place please reveal that to me and help me to change it. I want to be focused properly on you and on the things that are eternally significant.

Amen

Week Thirty Eight
Pregnancy Week 40

Only 4% of women give birth on their estimated due date and a majority of women give birth after their due date. Your baby is around 7.5 pounds (3400 g) and the placenta weighs in at 1.5 pounds. Although she seems complete, your baby's immune system is still strengthening.

At this point, it is a delicate hormone balance that will determine when you go into labor. Your body is producing substances called prostaglandins in response to a hormone produced in your baby and the placenta. The prostaglandins ripen the cervix for dilation and help to increase the frequency of contractions.

You are producing more estrogen each day than a non-pregnant woman produces in a year. The increase in estrogen makes the uterus more sensitive to oxytocin, the chemical in your body that helps cause contractions. This is why you feel more frequent Braxton-Hicks contractions. The more frequent uterine activity combined with the soften cervix can dilate your cervix a bit before labor truly begins.

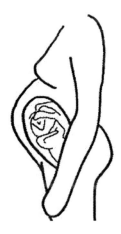

Chanukah

It is amazing that when following the gestational feast timeline set out by Zola Levitt, Chanukah occurs around the time your baby will be born. Even more amazing is this is not a one day feast, but an 8 day celebration which takes into account the normal variations in the length of gestation.

The Festival of Lights is the remembrance of God's provision for his people when they were in need. Not only did God lead the Maccabees to victory, but the oil that should have only been enough for one day burned for eight days. The significance of this to your pregnancy then would be God's ability to meet your needs during labor.

Sometimes it seems easier for God to perform a miracle or be in control of a situation so far from your everyday life, like a war in ancient Israel. But God is alive and active today. He is as much in control of what is happening with your body as he was with keeping the lamps burning.

That doesn't mean your labor will be miraculously easy. Remember, God kept the lamps burning, but that happened in the midst of a war. In labor, God can and will supply your needs, but you will still be moving through the process of giving birth. The presence of pain or discomfort or a medical emergency does not mean God is not with you. The biggest miracle of all is that God can give you peace even in the middle of a difficult labor; he can keep your lamps burning.   ——

Please see the acknowledgement page in the front of the book for more information about Zola Levitt Ministries, Inc.

Prayer Guide: Week 38

PRAYING FOR HEALTH

Mom:
Hormonal balance for labor
Cervical changes
Braxton-Hicks contractions

Baby:
Immune system maturation
Hormonal balance for labor

PRAYING THE BIBLE

And my God will meet all your needs according to his glorious riches in Christ Jesus. *Philippians 4:19*

The Lord protects the simple hearted; when I was in great need, he saved me. *Psalm 116:6*

SAMPLE PRAYER

Lord,

How amazing that the festival of lights is my reminder you will be with me in labor. No matter what happens, please don't let me forget you are with me and watching over me. Help me to remember you will supply my needs.

As I wait for labor to begin, please keep the image of the lamps in my head. I trust you will demonstrate a miracle in me through this labor. Please open my eyes so I can see it.

Amen

Week Thirty Nine
Pregnancy Week 41

If you have made it this far in pregnancy, you may be beginning to wonder if the due date was miscalculated. It makes little difference to your baby what day ends the average length of pregnancy; he is waiting for the hormones in your body to change enough for labor to start.

Although there is little concern for a baby's well being at this point, there are some things you can do to help reassure yourself. Your caregiver may offer you a non-stress test during which you will be given some medication to force contractions and then watch your baby's heart rate as a way to check her overall health.

Another test you can do is called Fetal Kick Counting. To do this you will choose a time, and then count how long it takes for your baby to make 10 different movements. You will do this every day to see a pattern. If your baby remains as active, you can be reassured of her overall health.

Even knowing your little one is healthy doesn't prevent you from feeling awkward when people make comments about you "still" being pregnant. Another common concern is where you will be when labor begins, and knowing it could begin at any time. Less than 15% of labors begin with the breaking of the bag of waters, and most labors progress slowly enough in the early stages that you don't have to worry about getting back home before you are too uncomfortable. Just live your life as normally as possible, being sure to stay well rested, well nourished and well hydrated.

Weary

Let us not become weary in doing good, for at the proper time we will reap a harvest if we do not give up. Galatians 6:9

I know you are tired. I know you feel weak and uncomfortable, but don't give up! Do your best to stay healthy for you and your baby. Follow the principles of good nutrition and exercise, prepare yourself for giving birth and spend time with God every day. You have come so far, don't stop now!

Remember, at the proper time you will reap a harvest if you do not give up. But you need to wait for that proper time. You cannot pick crops before they are ready, they would be useless as food. The harvest you are waiting for is so much more important than grain. Your body houses the eternal soul of a child of God. Do you have any idea how important you are to the kingdom of God? Of course you will be under attack now, because if the enemy can pull you away from God he has also pulled your child away from God.

Pray with confidence that God will protect you. He will not allow you to struggle through trials without allowing you to rely on his strength. God can and will give you the patience and peace you need to wait for the day when your child is ready to be born.

Prayer Guide: Week 39

PRAYING FOR HEALTH

Mom:
Hormonal balance for labor
Tests for well-being
Emotional comfort

Baby:
Hormonal balance for labor
Positioned properly for birth

PRAYING THE BIBLE

No temptation has seized you except what is common to man. And God is faithful; he will not let you be tempted beyond what you can bear. But when you are tempted, he will also provide a way out so that you can stand up under it. *1 Corinthians 10:13*

But if we hope for what we do not yet have, we wait for it patiently. *Romans 8:25*

SAMPLE PRAYER

Lord,

I know you are in control, and I know I can trust you. Knowing that doesn't seem to stop me from feeling weary as I wait for labor to begin. Please give me the rest I need and the strength I need to continue to wait in good health.

Help me to keep a good attitude as I wait. Bring people into my life who will encourage rather than discourage me. Refresh my spirit daily so I can continue to be a reflection of your light even though I feel tired.

Amen

Week Forty
Pregnancy Week 42

Over 98% of all babies are born by the end of this week. If you have not started labor by the end of the week, your caregiver may suggest some ways to help labor begin. The concern is a condition called post-dates in which the placenta no longer functions well and the baby is put at risk. Being overdue by itself is not a problem, however postdates only seems to happen in babies older than 40 weeks gestation.

If your baby has been born, you are probably making all the common adjustments to being a new mother, or the mother of a newborn. For some women the transition to sleepless nights is overwhelming, for others the frequent breastfeeding can seem too much to handle.

As you move through this first month of mothering your baby, be sure to ask for help when it is needed. One of the risk factors for postpartum depression is a lack of support or help during the first weeks with a new baby. Although it can be humbling to let others do things for you, it allows you the time you need to learn about and bond with your new baby. And remember, the people who love you and care about you want to participate in any way they can. They may just be waiting for you to ask them.

Adjusting to Motherhood

Being a new mother can be simply overwhelming. You don't get the sleep you are used to. You spend almost every waking moment meeting the needs of your child who is completely dependant on you. Your other responsibilities seem to be piling up and it is easy to feel you have gotten in way over your head.

Take some time today to sit quietly holding and rocking your baby. Let yourself feel the emotions sweeping over you, the tremendous love and concern you have for your child; the amazement at the potential your child has; the instincts you have to do anything necessary to protect this child; the way you want to fulfill her every need to keep her comfortable and healthy. Then let yourself realize God feels that same love for you.

God will not leave you. He will provide you with what you need to do the job he has given you. You may not get sleep, but God does not promise you sleep, he said he would give you rest. You may not be able to eat the way you are used to, but God does not promise you food, he said he would sustain you. You may feel weak, but God did not promise to make you strong, he said he would be your strength in weakness.

Let God take care of you, let God fulfill your needs so you can meet the needs of your baby. Trust God to supply you with the time, energy and resources you need to do the job of caring for his child. And relax a little, because you are not responsible for the whole world. In fact, according to the Jewish law a new mother is ritually unclean for at least eight days and cannot be purified for another thirty. Because of the ceremonial uncleanness, the new mother should limit her activities. God knew you would need to focus on the new baby and recover from the birth. Accept this time he has given you to do just that.

Prayer Guide: Week 40

PRAYING FOR HEALTH

Mom:
Wisdom about starting labor
Adjustment to motherhood
Postpartum depression

Baby:
Health
Adjust to life outside mom

PRAYING THE BIBLE

I have set the Lord always before me.
Because he is at my right hand,
I will not be shaken.
Therefore my heart is glad and my tongue rejoices;
my body also will rest secure,
because you will not abandon me to the grave,
nor will you let your Holy One see decay. *Psalm 16:8-10*

My soul finds rest in God alone; my salvation comes from him.
Psalm 62:1

SAMPLE PRAYER

Lord,

Please help me to trust in you. Be my strength and give me rest. Please fulfill all my needs so I can take care of my new baby.

Even when I don't sleep, please continue to give me rest. Even when I don't seem to be able to sit for a meal, please keep my body sustained. Even when I have no strength left, please be my strength.

Amen

Part Three
Staying Comfortable

May your unfailing love be my comfort,
according to your promise to your servant.

Psalm 119:76

Staying Comfortable

The following pages contain common concerns and symptoms of pregnancy listed alphabetically. Included with each topic is an explanation of why this occurs and some ways other mothers have found relief from the symptoms.

Some of the normal changes you will experience during pregnancy may feel uncomfortable, but a normal healthy pregnant woman should be able to deal with these minor discomforts without too much difficulty. If you are struggling with feeling comfortable, try some of the suggestions in this section. You may find a simple solution that works well for you.

If you continue to struggle with being uncomfortable, take some time to evaluate not just your physical health, but your emotional health too. Stress builds, making it more difficult to handle things that would otherwise be easy for you to handle. Be sure to share any fears or concerns you have with a trusted confidant.

If you are concerned about something happening to you physically or emotionally, it is always appropriate to seek the advice of your doctor or midwife. Her training has prepared her to help you recognize the difference between what is normal and what is not normal.

Backache in Pregnancy

Several factors work together to cause backaches in mid to late pregnancy. Some women respond to the changing center of gravity by pulling their shoulders back, which puts pressure on the lower back. Wearing shoes with a heel will further exaggerate the arching, causing worse backaches.

The ligaments holding the uterus in place are attached to the back. As the uterus grows, this added weight pulling on the back may cause backaches.

When your baby begins to descend into the pelvis, the head can cause pressure on the pelvis which may be felt as a backache.

WHAT MIGHT HELP

- ✓ Check your posture to be sure your back is not arched.
- ✓ Try pelvic tilting, it stretches the muscles of the back and re-aligns the uterus.
- ✓ Have someone massage, or just put pressure on your lower back.
- ✓ Avoid shoes with heels.
- ✓ Be sure to rest when you have been on your feet for an extended period of time.

Bladder Issues in Pregnancy

The pressure of your growing uterus and a heightened metabolic rate cause increased frequency of urination. It seems to be more of a problem in the first and last trimesters, when the uterus takes more room in the pelvis. For some women, the increased weight of the uterus stresses the pelvic floor muscle causing incontinence.

The progesterone that is working to ensure you stay pregnant relaxes smooth muscle (like your urinary tract). This can increase your chances of developing a urinary tract infection, bladder infection and kidney infection.

WHAT MIGHT HELP

- ✓ Do your pelvic floor (kegel) exercises. They strengthen this muscle to help it work properly even with the increased weight of the uterus.
- ✓ Keep drinking water. Being dehydrated won't decrease the frequency of bathroom breaks, but it can cause discomfort, fatigue, and increases your risks for other problems.
- ✓ Go to the bathroom regularly, don't try to hold it.
- ✓ If you feel a burning or stinging sensation when you urinate, you may have an infection. Seek the advice of your caregiver.
- ✓ Don't sit with your legs crossed or wear tight, restrictive clothing. These things may encourage a back-up in your urinary tract causing an infection

Bleeding Gums in Pregnancy

Your blood volume increases when you are pregnant, which can cause some swelling in tissues with very small blood vessels, such as the nasal passages and gums. During the second half of pregnancy, tender gums may react to vigorous tooth brushing by bleeding.

WHAT MIGHT HELP

- ✓ Switch to a soft bristle tooth brush.
- ✓ Brush your teeth more gently; floss no more than once a day.
- ✓ Do have your teeth professionally cleaned at least once while pregnant.
- ✓ Check your diet for adequate amounts of Vitamin C, a vital nutrient for tissue healing.
- ✓ Try using a mouthwash to remove the taste of blood from your mouth.

Blotchy Skin in Pregnancy

Your skin may appear darkened or blotchy on your face, breasts and abdomen. This is due to your high hormone levels. Some experts feel this is normal, others believe it may signal nutritional deficits.

WHAT MIGHT HELP

- ✓ Avoid spending time in the sun, which makes the blotches darker and more pronounced.
- ✓ Check your diet for adequate levels of folic acid.
- ✓ The blotches will go away after your baby is born, but if they bother you cover them with a concealer.

Breasts in Pregnancy

Mammary glands are the only glands that mature after puberty. Instead, they mature during pregnancy. The growth and development of these glands can cause the surrounding area to be sensitive to the touch or sore. This is normal and is most common during early pregnancy and near the end of pregnancy.

It is normal for your breasts to leak fluid as your mammary glands mature and begin to make colostrum. It is also normal for the breasts not to leak. Whether your breasts are leaking or not leaking has no impact on your ability to breastfeed.

WHAT MIGHT HELP

- ✓ Stand in the shower and let the warm water massage your breasts.
- ✓ Be sure to wear a bra with good support, and have the fit checked as your breasts may have grown.
- ✓ Avoid the breasts during intimacy; they are usually only sensitive for a few weeks.
- ✓ Try wearing a bra at night, the extra support may feel better.
- ✓ Put breast pads inside your bra to absorb the moisture.
- ✓ Wash off dried colostrum with warm water, soap is not necessary and may dry out the skin.

Constipation in Pregnancy

Your heightened progesterone level will cause the smooth muscle of your body, such as your digestive system, to relax and become sluggish. Add to this the pressure on your intestinal tract from the growing uterus and it should seem obvious why the whole system is a little slow.

WHAT MIGHT HELP

- ✓ Try pelvic tilting or going for a walk. Both can stimulate the digestive system.
- ✓ Check your diet to be sure you are getting enough fiber and water.
- ✓ Put a low stool under you feet in the bathroom. This will put you in more of a squat position which opens the outlet of the pelvis making it easier for material to pass.
- ✓ Try eating raw fruits and veggies.

Contractions in Pregnancy

Like any muscle, your uterus gets stronger with exercise. While pregnant, you will experience uterine exercise as Braxton-Hicks contractions. These are usually not a problem, as they are mild contractions that don't last very long. They may seem to have a regular rhythmic pattern, such as every 10 minutes, but they will not get more intense, closer together or longer like labor contractions will. Most women find they become increasingly frequent in the last months of pregnancy.

WHAT MIGHT HELP

- ✓ If you have been moving around, sit and rest. If you have been sitting or resting, get up and walk around. Changing your activity may stop Braxton-Hicks contractions.
- ✓ Eat or drink something. Your body can start contractions if the baby needs food. Dehydration can start contractions that look like labor, but are non-productive (they don't open the cervix).
- ✓ Ignore them. They are not an indicator of when you will begin labor, so if possible, just ignore what is happening and go about your regular routine.
- ✓ Relax and do abdominal breathing. These contractions are good for your baby (the massage helps respiration), good for you (they make the uterus stronger for labor) and will end shortly. It might be a good time to practice your relaxation.
- ✓ Contact your doula for some reassurance. She can help you understand the difference between pre-labor and contractions that will become labor.

Faintness in Pregnancy

Your blood volume increases during pregnancy, and the high progesterone levels relax your blood vessels to prevent high blood pressure. However, the relaxed vessels can slow down your circulation enough that you feel faint when you stand up suddenly.

Another factor to look for is your body temperature. When your body is overheating, your blood vessels dilate and move closer to your skin to let some of your deep body heat escape. If this happens to your already relaxed blood vessels, you may feel dizzy, light-headed or faint.

WHAT MIGHT HELP

- ✓ Take cooler baths and showers that don't raise your body temperature.
- ✓ Be sure to do deep abdominal breathing to get your blood fully oxygenated.
- ✓ Be sure you are not skipping meals, and have snacks if necessary. You metabolism is in over-drive and you need to keep your blood sugar levels up.
- ✓ Don't stand for long periods of time. Plan your activities in such a way you can move around and rest.
- ✓ Frequent faintness may be an indicator of anemia, low iron levels in your blood. This is a common problem in pregnancy and can often be treated by a change in diet or by using an iron supplement. Be sure to talk to your caregiver about your options.

Fatigue in Pregnancy

Your metabolism has increased significantly as your body builds your baby, so your body's energy demands have greatly increased. The changing hormone levels are also very demanding on your body. These changes work together to cause you to be very tired in early pregnancy.

In the third trimester, you may find the extra effort it takes to carry around the extra weight, combined with the difficulty sleeping at night, makes you tired. It is important to eat enough for your energy demands, especially Iron.

WHAT MIGHT HELP

- ✓ Ask your doctor to check your blood iron levels. If they are low you will need to supplement with vitamins to regain your energy.
- ✓ Be diligent about your eating. You must eat enough food every day, and you must eat a balanced diet every day.
- ✓ Take rest times during the day. Sometimes 10 minutes of abdominal breathing with your feet up can be as good as a long nap.
- ✓ Drink plenty of water. One of the effects of dehydration is to make you tired.
- ✓ Get some exercise every day. Exercise helps keep your energy levels higher during pregnancy and increases your stamina for labor.

Hemorrhoids in Pregnancy

Hemorrhoids are varicose veins of the rectum. You may experience them from straining too hard when using the bathroom. They can be uncomfortable or itchy when you sit.

WHAT MIGHT HELP

- ✓ Put a low stool under your feet while you use the toilet. This realigns the pelvis to make using the bathroom easier.
- ✓ Be sure you are getting adequate water and fiber in your diet.
- ✓ Avoid constipation, which will cause you to push harder when going to the bathroom.
- ✓ Try walking and pelvic tilting as natural stimulants for the bowel.
- ✓ Ice the sore area for some comfort and relief.
- ✓ Try taking shallow, warm baths to soak the area for some comfort and relief.
- ✓ Fill a jar with cotton balls, cover them with witch hazel and stick it in your refrigerator. After you go to the bathroom, stick a few cotton balls on the affected area, and leave them there for 20-30 minutes.

Heartburn and Indigestion in Pregnancy

Your growing uterus puts pressure on your digestive system and your digestive system is sluggish. These two factors may cause you to feel uncomfortable after you eat. Although it is considered normal in pregnancy, changes in your eating habits may help to relieve some of the discomfort.

WHAT MIGHT HELP

- ✓ Eat smaller meals. This will decrease the pressure on your digestive system and may make digesting easier.
- ✓ Eat more frequent meals. This will prevent dips in blood sugar that may cause indigestion. Drink more water and eat adequate amounts of fiber to help move the food through the digestive system.
- ✓ Go for a walk after dinner. Walking is a natural way to aid digestion.
- ✓ Try pelvic tilting, which moves the uterus into a different position and may give your body enough room to complete digestion.
- ✓ Pay attention to the way you feel after you eat different foods. If some foods or types of food make you feel ill, minimize them in your diet.
- ✓ If you are finding yourself frequently sick after eating, talk to your caregiver. You may have developed a digestive problem or sensitivity to a particular food.

Leg Cramps in Pregnancy

Leg cramps may be caused by a combination of two issues. First, some experts believe inadequate levels of calcium in your diet can lead to leg cramps. Secondly, decreased circulation to your legs can cause cramping. Leg cramps tend to be more common in the last half of pregnancy.

WHAT MIGHT HELP

✓ Be sure to eat calcium rich foods. Calcium is less easily absorbed when you are pregnant, so your need for it increases.

✓ Don't wear clothing that might restrict blood flow to your legs.

✓ Try sitting tailor-style (cross-legged). This position naturally helps prevent pelvic congestion and improves circulation to the legs.

✓ Try walking and pelvic tilting as natural ways to improve circulation to the legs.

✓ If you get a leg cramp, try to massage it out or use heat on it.

✓ With calf cramps, push your heel down and your toes up.

Decreased Libido in Pregnancy

Physical discomfort, fatigue, hormonal changes and a changing body image work together to cause a decreased desire for physical intimacy when pregnant. Some couples are afraid to continue with sexual relations for fear it may hurt the baby.

WHAT MIGHT HELP

- ✓ Understand that intimacy, sexual play and intercourse are all safe and healthy during a normal pregnancy.
- ✓ Try new positions that take the pressure off your abdomen and back to make intimacy more comfortable.
- ✓ You may find that it is more comfortable to spend your time in sexual play rather than intercourse.
- ✓ Accept that there may be days you simply cannot get your body to want to be touched.
- ✓ Focus on activities that avoid overly sensitive or sore parts of your body.
- ✓ Make sure you are getting adequate exercise. Exercise will improve your stamina and your overall feelings of well-being.

Lightening in Pregnancy

Towards the end of your pregnancy, your baby will move down into the pelvis to prepare for labor. This is called engagement, dropping or lightening. Having the baby engaged in the pelvis is not an indicator that you are going into labor.

For some women, the baby does not engage in the pelvis until labor starts.

WHAT MIGHT HELP

✓ Don't worry too much. Having dropped or not dropped doesn't change when your baby will be ready to be born.

Moodiness in Pregnancy

Your fluctuating hormone levels make you more susceptible to moodiness when you are pregnant. Near the end of pregnancy, your altered body image, fatigue and concerns about the upcoming labor can add to the moodiness.

WHAT MIGHT HELP

- ✓ Allow yourself time to cry, you may find yourself with renewed energy afterwards.
- ✓ Seek out support from friends and family. Have at least one person you can share your concerns with.
- ✓ Slow down your schedule; be sure to give yourself enough time to rest.
- ✓ Be extra careful about eating well, poor nutrition will only make you less able to handle everyday stress.

Nausea and Vomiting in Pregnancy

Nausea and Vomiting in pregnancy, commonly called morning sickness, can actually occur at any time of day. Experts are unsure of the exact reasons for it, but believe it may be due to the rapid fluctuations in blood sugar levels, or a reaction to changing hormones. About half of all pregnant women experience morning sickness.

WHAT MIGHT HELP

- ✓ Eat smaller meals more frequently to keep your blood sugar levels constant.
- ✓ Eat something right before you go to bed, preferably a protein food which will take longer to digest.
- ✓ If you wake up at night to use the bathroom, stop by the kitchen and eat a small snack to keep your blood sugar level up.
- ✓ Avoid foods that trigger nausea for you.
- ✓ Try eating the foods you crave, within reason.
- ✓ Keep crackers near your bed for you to nibble on before you get up.
- ✓ Try drinking fluids after your meal, not during.

Nosebleeds in Pregnancy

The increased blood volume may cause the small and sensitive vessels in your nose to break easily during pregnancy.

WHAT MIGHT HELP

- ✓ Pinch your nose to stop a bleed.
- ✓ Be sure to eat a diet rich in Vitamin C to promote tissue health and healing.
- ✓ Blow your nose gently to prevent the breaking of blood vessels.
- ✓ Use a humidifier or vaporizer to keep your home adequately moist during dry months.
- ✓ Some women will rub a small amount of petroleum jelly in each nostril before going to bed.

Pelvic Pressure in Pregnancy

Your enlarging uterus puts pressure on your pelvis. The sciatic nerve can be affected as the pelvis relaxes and stretches. This would feel like pain that starts in the pelvis and continues down the thigh.

Sharp pains on either side of your abdomen could be the stretching of the ligaments that support your uterus.

WHAT MIGHT HELP

- ✓ Use heat to dull the pain, and massage to relax it away.
- ✓ Change your position, you may be able to get the baby to move and thereby change the way he puts pressure on your pelvis.
- ✓ Try pelvic tilting to change the baby's position.
- ✓ Talk to your doctor about other options you may have if the pain becomes frequent or unbearable.

Feeling the Baby Move in Pregnancy

Quickening is the term given to the time in pregnancy when you can feel the baby move. This is generally around the 4th or 5th month.

Once you understand what it feels like when the baby moves, you should be feeling the baby move every day. Babies tend to be more active when mom slows down and relaxes. The theory is that when mom is active the movement of the pelvis rocks the baby to sleep. As baby grows, the movements will shift from kicks to rolls or twists.

WHAT MIGHT HELP

- ✓ You will not hurt the baby by pushing back gently. Go ahead and play with him.
- ✓ If baby's kicks are uncomfortable (such as ones to the ribs), try to do some pelvic tilting or walking to see if you can get the baby to shift positions.

Shortness of Breath in Pregnancy

Your need for oxygen increases during pregnancy, but your uterus expands restricting the amount of air your lungs can take in with each breath.

WHAT MIGHT HELP

- ✓ Do deep abdominal breathing, trying to get the most air possible with each breath.
- ✓ Change your position, you may find upright positions give you more room to breathe.
- ✓ Slow down or reduce your activity level to give your body a chance to catch up.

Sleepless Nights in Pregnancy

When your belly is large and you cannot find a comfortable position in bed, sleep becomes difficult. In addition to the physical discomfort of the growing belly, you may wake up several times a night to use the bathroom.

WHAT MIGHT HELP

- ✓ Try pelvic tilting just before you go to bed. It pulls the uterus into a better position so the bladder is not as compressed.
- ✓ Use lots of pillows to support your belly, back and legs.
- ✓ Try propping your upper body up more by using pillows.
- ✓ Experiment with couches and armchairs in your home to see if you can find a comfortable position in one of them.

Stretch Marks in Pregnancy

There is no way to prevent stretch marks. They are scar tissues caused by the over-stretching of the skin. You may experience them on your abdomen, breasts or upper legs.

WHAT MIGHT HELP

- ✓ Eat foods rich in vitamin E and Vitamin C. These nutrients are necessary for healthy skin.
- ✓ Keeping your skin moisturized won't prevent stretch marks, but it can help prevent the dry itchiness some women feel as the skin stretches.
- ✓ Don't waste money on treatments. They will not prevent stretch marks, and they will minimize on their own after your baby is born.

Swelling in Pregnancy

Swelling is a normal part of pregnancy. Your circulatory system is relaxed and sluggish, which can contribute to fluid retention. Swelling is also a healthy way your body helps support the extra blood volume in the week or two before you give birth.

WHAT MIGHT HELP

- ✓ Drink plenty of water. Dehydration will not reduce swelling, since swelling comes from excess water in your tissues, not your blood.
- ✓ Take frequent rest periods when you have to be on your feet for long amounts of time.
- ✓ Don't wear clothing that is restrictive.
- ✓ Sit in the cross-legged position whenever possible, and do pelvic tilting daily to promote good circulation.
- ✓ Be sure to discuss concerns about swelling or any sudden swelling with your midwife.

Vaginal Discharge in Pregnancy

Your cervix produces fluids during pregnancy that help to keep the vaginal canal clean and infection free. This increased moisture and the change in acid levels of the vagina make the area easily susceptible to a yeast infection. The increased moisture also makes the skin of the perineum brittle and susceptible to tearing as your baby is born.

WHAT MIGHT HELP

- ✓ Wear cotton panties, which have a tendency to be more absorbent.
- ✓ Do not wear tight clothing around the perineum. This forces the fluids back up the vagina increasing your risks for infection.
- ✓ A panty-liner may help minimize discomfort from moisture.
- ✓ If possible, go panty-less in the evenings or at night to allow the vaginal skin time to dry out.
- ✓ Using soap will only make the skin more dried out and brittle. Try cleansing with warm water and a cloth only.
- ✓ If you do get a yeast infection, contact your caregiver right away to start treatments. A yeast infection can be transferred to the baby during birth.

Varicose Veins in Pregnancy

Varicose veins occur when your already sluggish circulatory system is constricted due to the pressure of your growing uterus and the increased blood volume.

WHAT MIGHT HELP

- ✓ Try exercises for your feet and legs that may help improve circulation.
- ✓ Take frequent rest periods when you have to be on your feet for long amounts of time.
- ✓ Don't wear clothing that is restrictive, or stay in positions that might cut off your circulation.
- ✓ Sit in the cross-legged position whenever possible, and do pelvic tilting daily to promote good circulation.

Weight Gain in Pregnancy

As your baby grows, and your body changes to support the baby, you will gain weight.

WHAT MIGHT HELP

- ✓ Instead of focusing on how much weight you are gaining, focus on eating well and getting adequate exercise.
- ✓ Put all your scales in a closet and don't get them out for a year.
- ✓ Don't jump right into maternity clothes, which will be too big early in your pregnancy. Instead buy some clothes a size larger than you usually wear. Better yet, borrow them from a friend.
- ✓ Don't use pregnancy as an excuse to feed your appetite rather than your hunger. Overeating will make you feel sluggish and heavy, and it will not help your baby.
- ✓ If you are having trouble gaining weight because of illness, focus your eating efforts on high protein foods.

Index

R

Relaxin, *see Hormones*

S

Salt, 121
Sleeplessness, 191
Squatting, *see Pregnancy Exercises*
Stretch Marks, 219
Swelling, 42, 64, 143, 200, 220

T

Trimester
    First, 41, 92, 98, 113
    Second, 39, 98, 104
    Third, 42, 146, 206

U

Umbilical Cord, 83, 86, 104, 113, 182
Urinary Tract
    Frequent Urination, 113, 199
    Infection, 62, 199
Uterus, 4, 5, 161

V

Vagina, 4, 6, 77, 221
    Discharge, 62, 65, 116
    Infection, 62
Varicose Veins, 207
vernix caseosa, 122, 124, 167, 182
Vomiting, *see Indigestion*

W

Weight Gain, 31, 42, 64, 98, 116, 118, 166, 170, 172, 179

About the Author

Jennifer Vanderlaan is a childbirth educator and doula living in upstate New York. She created the Birthing Naturally website, co-founded Cascade Christian Childbirth Association and developed a local volunteer doula ministry. Her materials, including *The Lord of Birth* Bible Study, are used in childbirth classes around the country.

Jennifer married her husband, Jeff, in 1995. They moved from Michigan to New York so Jeff could serve as minister to the students at The University at Albany. They have been blessed with two children, Josette and Jaron. They have experienced two normal, natural births; one at home and one in a hospital.

Jennifer writes out of her desire to share what she has learned with other women. The material for 40 Weeks is a combination of information presented in her childbirth classes and notes from the margin of her Bible. For more of Jennifer's writings about pregnancy and childbirth, please visit her website where you will find information for staying healthy, preparing for labor and natural childbirth comfort measures.

www.birthingnaturally.net

If you like 40 Weeks, you'll love

The Lord of Birth

Devotional Bible Study for Pregnancy

The process of pregnancy and giving birth doesn't change because you are a Christian, but the way you handle it does. As a Christian, you have a special gift in the faith and trust you have in Jesus Christ and the love of God. The Lord of Birth is a 10 week study exploring what the Bible says about the subjects important to a pregnant woman, and how your relationship with Jesus will impact your labor.

Intended to build your faith and trust in God, encourage you through pregnancy and prepare you to give birth, the Lord of Birth is perfect for a small group or individual study.

Find more information about The Lord of Birth and other books written by Jennifer Vanderlaan at:

www.birthingnaturally.net